DAVID TAYLOR'S

ZOO

around us

PIPIT
PRESS

Abbreviations

mm	millimetre
cm	centimetre
m	metre
km	kilometre
ha	hectare
gm	gram
kg	kilogram

Published in Great Britain by Pipit Press in 1990.
Pipit Press is an imprint of Boxtree Limited,
36 Tavistock Street, London WC2E 7PB

ISBN 1 85283 029 8

Edited by Graham Eyre
Designed by Graham Dudley
Jacket designed by Groom & Pickerill
Typeset by Servis Filmsetting Limited, Manchester

Acknowledgements

Photographs on pages 34, 86 by courtesy of Oxford Scientific Films; pages 68, 70, 71, 76, 83, 138 Bruce Coleman Limited; pages 80, 140, 151 London School of Hygiene and Tropical Medicine (Electron Microscopy Laboratory); page 155 Mansell Collection; page 173 London School of Hygiene and Tropical Medicine (Dept. of Medical Protozoology).

Contents

Introduction

My dictionary says that the word 'zoo' refers to the Zoological Gardens in London and also any similar collection of animals elsewhere. Nothing is nicer than to go to a city zoo, on say, a bright and crisp Sunday morning in autumn, to watch the lions, languid and aristocratic as they recline in the pale sunlight, to smell the unmistakable smell of elephant, to marvel at the sealions darting like arrows through the water, to look at and to be looked at by animals strange and rare, delicate and fierce, from the four quarters of the globe. Here is an aardvark – what do you know about aardvarks? There goes a pangolin in his oriental armour, and what sort of creature is this mara – half giant guinea pig, half hare?

Yes, zoos have fascinated me since I first went to the old Belle Vue Zoo in Manchester as a small boy, little knowing that I would one day become a Zoo Vet travelling round the world attending to every kind of wild animal from killer whale to koala, Komodo dragon to crocodile. But some time ago it occurred to me that the zoo in its broadest sense is not confined to Regent's Park or Windsor Safari Park or Chessington World of Adventures. Sure, lemurs and lynxes and lions and llamas are exotic and intriguing beasts, but they have no monopoly on excitement and interest. All animals are brilliantly designed to do the job they do best, to survive against all odds. If they weren't brilliant they wouldn't be around now; they or their ancestors would have perished on the long inexorable march of evolution. Of course a blue whale or a giant panda is a marvellous creation of nature – but no more so than, say, a sparrow or a house mouse. Life, the engine that throbs within every living organism, is *the* big miracle and mystery.

What is more, living things are all around us. You don't have to go to the zoo to see animals. They have come to us; they live with and near us. So in a very real sense we live in a zoo – no matter that our address may be a city street, an apartment block in some new town, or a cottage in a peaceful country hamlet. All we have to do to see the amazing inhabitants of our local zoo is *look*.

In this book I deal with some of the animals that are so close, so common to us, that they are frequently overlooked. Many are so familiar that we don't bother to learn anything about their ways, their lifestyles.

The first part goes out into the garden to find ten animals among those that we are sure to meet if only we open our eyes.

The second part is devoted to animals that enjoy sharing man's dwellings. They lodge in the house – but don't pay poll tax, water rates or electricity bills!

The third part is the section for 'townies' who all too easily forget that concrete and iron, tower blocks and supermarkets, high streets and civic centres still constitute an environment in which animals of a surprisingly wide variety can live and multiply with great success.

In the final part you will find animals, many of which are too tiny to be seen without the aid of a microscope. They are abundant and make their home, guess where, on and in your body!

The zoo then, is everywhere. We are never, thank goodness, without the company of animals. All that remains is for you – and me – to look, learn and appreciate the rich pattern of life that envelopes us.

Discover the animals which live in your garden

The Blue Tit

One of the handsomest of Britain's garden birds is this little dandy in its blue, yellow, black and white gear. If blue tits were a rare tropical species, folk would no doubt praise their beauty more loudly. As it is, the blue tit is the fourth most common bird to be seen in gardens in Britain. Only the blackbird, starling and house sparrow are more common.

The name 'blue tit' is a shortened form of 'blue titmouse' and 'titmouse' comes from Old English. 'Tit' means tiny and 'mouse' (nothing to do with Mickey Mouse!) is a corruption of 'mose', meaning a small bird. Tits, of which there are 42 species worldwide, are typical insect-eating birds of scrub and woodland. Our friend the blue tit occurs widely throughout Europe and Asia.

The blue tit is ever active, tending to flit about from branch to branch, but able to fly long distances too. It is an expert at hanging upside-down, which enables it to hunt caterpillars on the underside of leaves. You can watch its acrobatics for yourself if you have a hanging container of bird food (nuts, suet or one of the special mixtures available from the pet or garden shop) in your garden or back-yard – especially in the winter months, when there are not many insects about and blue tits rely more on seeds and berries for food. At the end of summer, blue tits tend to leave the garden and go hunting in groups in woodland, but they are back as soon as the winter cold sets in.

A pair of blue-tit parents feeding their nestlings gather caterpillars at a rate of around 1 per minute. That means that over the whole period of raising their chicks they catch about 10,000 caterpillars! Another thing blue tits like is cream. They are often seen making short work of milk-bottle tops and helping themselves to the cream at the top of the bottle.

Blue-tit eggs are laid in clutches averaging 10 in number, but they can range from as few as 6 to as many as 24. The eggs, which are white with reddish-brown spots, are laid in April or May and hatch at a time when there are lots of caterpillars around for the chicks to eat. The incubation period – the time it takes for the eggs to hatch – is around 12–14 days and only the female sits on the eggs to hatch them.

About 1 month after the eggs hatch you may be lucky enough to watch the young birds trying to pluck up courage to leave the nest for the first time. To tempt her youngsters to fly, the mother bird sits on a convenient perch outside the nest with a plump caterpillar in her beak. She gives lots of encouragement to her children, saying in effect, 'Come on! You can do it, and here's the prize for the first one to prove it!' The first fledgling to leave the nest is the one who hesitates the least, but as soon as it

A blue tit, the fourth commonest bird in our garden, takes wing

Blue tits welcome feeding in winter

takes the plunge the others usually all fly out at once.

Like other tits, the blue tit nests in a hole in a tree-trunk or, if you are lucky, in your garden nest-box. The nest, which must be dry and draught-proof, is snugly lined with shreds of wool, feathers, hair, dried grass and moss. Nest-boxes should have a hole, metal-rimmed to prevent squirrels or woodpeckers from making it bigger, no more than 2.8 cm across (to keep out starlings and sparrows). Excellent ones can be obtained from the Royal Society for the Protection of Birds. The box should be placed in a position facing away from the prevailing winds at a height of between 1.5 and 2 m with plenty of space around – blue tits like to keep an eye open for their enemies.

Mother as flying-instructor!

Nest-boxes need sound construction

The Hedgehog

The hedgehog is not found in America but is widespread across Europe (except for most of Scandinavia and Iceland), Africa and Asia. There are 12 different species of hedgehog, including the *Western European* (the welcome visitor to our garden), the *long-eared hedgehog* and the *desert hedgehog*. The hedgehog is Britain's heaviest insectivore (insect-eating animal), weighing up to 1.4 kg, and measuring up to 30 cm in length. Hedgehog spines are actually very strong and flexible hairs and each adult animal sports about 6000 of them. They are 2–3 cm long, and each has a ball-like root to take shocks and a muscle that can pull it upright when the hedgehog is alarmed. Hedgehogs curl up into a ball at any sign of danger; that's why so many are tragically squashed on our roads. To curl up, a hedgehog uses a big oval shield of muscles that lies beneath the skin, over the back and down the sides of the body from head to tail. By

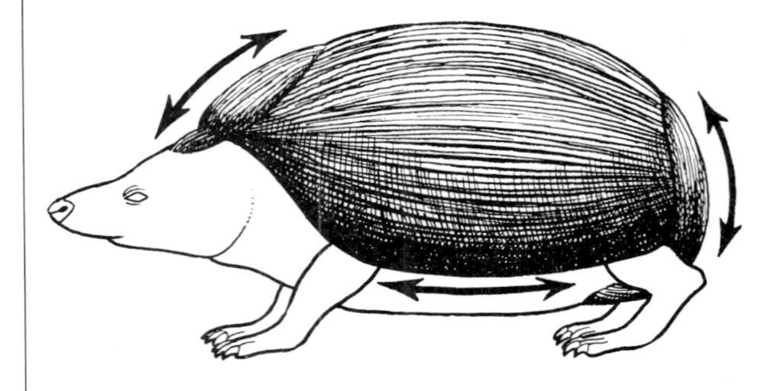

The muscle-shield of the hedgehog

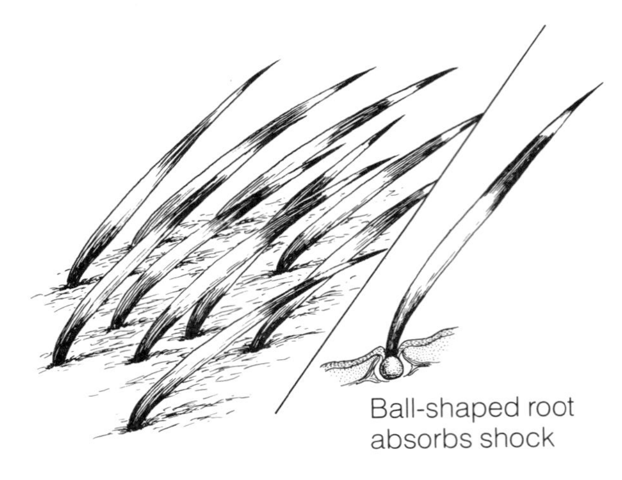

The shock-absorbing spine of a hedgehog

Heading for trouble

Our friend relishes some cat food

drawing in this shield, rather like pulling on the draw-string of a bag, the animal is instantly transformed into a spiky ball.

Hedgehogs are a gardener's friend, feeding on grubs, snails, caterpillars and other pests. Their favourite dish is worms, but they will also eat insects, woodlice, spiders, snails, frogs, toads, lizards and snakes, as well as berries, seeds or fallen fruit, though they do *not*, despite the charming legend, roll about in orchards spearing apples and pears on their prickles and then carrying them off to their larders. If you wish to put out food for a visiting hedgehog, try a saucer of milk, a bit of tinned cat or dog food, hard-boiled egg or cheese scraps. Hedgehogs do take wild birds' eggs if they come across them, but I don't believe they enter hen pens and steal or devour unbroken hens' eggs. As for the belief that hedgehogs suckle milk from cows, I think that's nonsense too. But sometimes a hedgehog may come across a cow with a little milk oozing from the teat of a full udder and lap up the drops.

Hedgehogs are very resistant to many kinds of poison. They can survive the bites of snakes that would kill 10 men and can eat wasps and bees without apparently being troubled by the insects' stings. They are also very noisy: they snort, hiss, cough, cackle, puff, grunt and scream. Nobody who has never heard a hedgehog would believe how noisy it can be. Hedgehogs have fairly good eyesight, but scientists report that they see the world only in shades of yellow! Their senses of hearing and smell are wonderfully well developed. When a hedgehog starts sniffing about, its nose begins to run and this helps the lining of its nostrils to pick up more efficiently the scents in the air.

Hedgehogs are fine swimmers but don't usually take a dip unless they have to. They are also surprisingly good climbers, and when they want to descend they simply let themselves roll

Hedgehogs are quite good climbers

down, using their spines as shock-absorbers. Few enemies can penetrate the spiky defensive ball of a curled-up hedgehog. Foxes and dogs stand little chance. Badgers, polecats or martens and large birds of prey (such as eagles) may sometimes be successful in forcing the ball open.

Hedgehogs hibernate in the winter, usually going to sleep in October and waking up in April. They pick a snug place called a 'hibernaculum' in a pile of dried leaves or a hole in a bank that they line with moss, bracken and leaves. To save energy and make sure the food stored in its body lasts till spring, the animal allows its temperature to drop and its heartbeat and breathing-rate slow right down. Beneath the skin of the hedgehog's back there is a special hibernation food source in the form of a layer of brown fat. This fat can release heat 20 times faster than ordinary fat and acts as if controlled by a thermostat. The lower the outside temperature, the more heat the brown fat releases into the sleeping hedgehog's body.

In spring a mother hedgehog makes

Napping away the winter months

A prickly defensive ball

her nest in some quiet spot, which may, if you are lucky, be beneath the floor of a garden shed. The baby hedgehogs are born between May and July, with a second litter sometimes produced during August and September after a pregnancy period of 30–40 days. There are normally 3–7 blind and deaf babies in a litter, each of them weighing about 9 gm. The spines of a newborn baby hedgehog are pale, soft and rubbery and are flattened into the skin, which is especially soggy with a high water content. $1\frac{1}{2}$–3 days after birth a second layer of spines begins to grow through the first spines, which are now standing upright. A baby hedgehog cannot roll into a ball until it is about 10 days old.

If you handle a hedgehog – perhaps nursing an injured one – be careful of any fleas and other parasites that there may be on the skin between the spines.

The Mole

The mole is that curious little fellow whose activities make lumps on the lawn. Because it works underground in the dark, and so is rarely seen, the mole is the least known of British garden mammals, though to my mind that makes it one of the most intriguing. It used to be trapped a lot for its velvety fur, used to make coats and trousers, but happily that has nearly stopped.

There are a number of different species of mole. The only one who lives in Britain is the *European mole*. In Spain, the Balkans and Turkey is found the *Mediterranean* mole, and the *Roman mole* lives in Italy and the Balkans. One of the most curious species is the *star-nosed mole* of North America, who looks as if he has a flower growing on the end of his snout.

A mole's body is long and perfectly shaped for the job of tunnelling. Its colour is a uniform black or dark grey with a short fur whose hairs are of even length and can lie flat in any direction (again, useful for tunnelling). The long, pointed muzzle is hairless except for the specialized, highly sensitive whiskers and can be wiggled about.

Moles have tiny but completely formed eyes. They cannot see very well, but their eyes are sensitive to changes in the brightness of light. Moles, which have no external ears, have a poorly developed sense of hearing, as you would expect of a creature who lives mostly underground, but they need and have a very good sense of smell. Glands in the animal's groin produce a smelly substance which is smeared by the belly fur onto the floor of the mole's underground tunnels, as a chemical sign that they are private property. The smell fades quite quickly and must be renewed regularly to keep up the effect. The most powerful sense of the mole, however, is that of touch. Life underground depends on a highly developed ability to feel your way round and recognize obstacles. The mole's

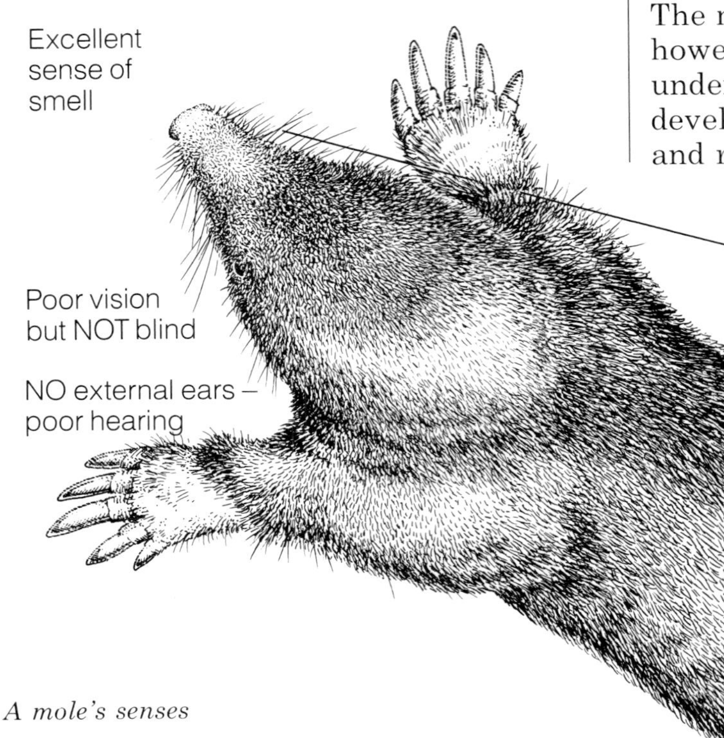

A mole's senses

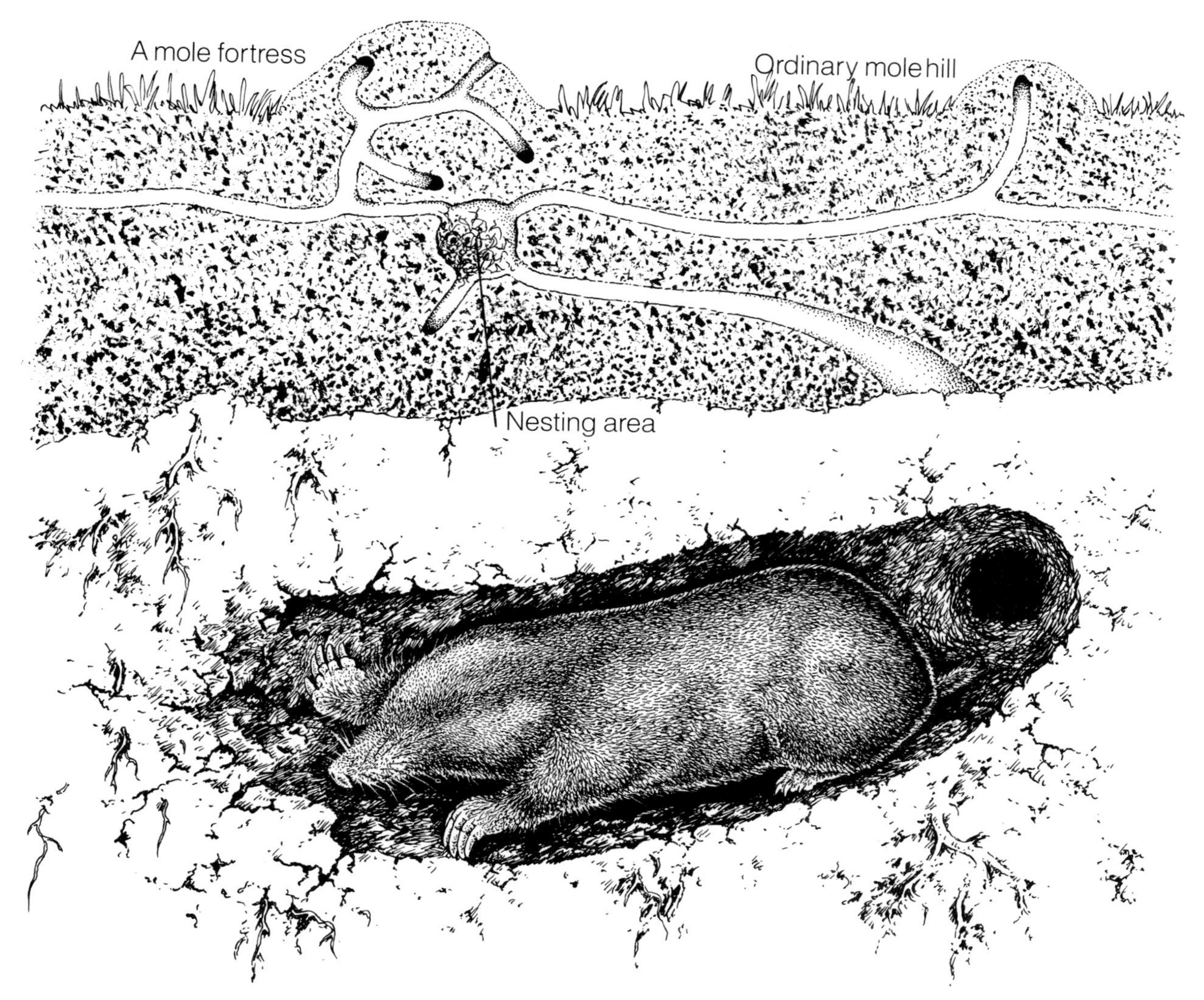

muzzle has nerve-endings and there are prominent, very sensitive whiskers on the muzzle and tail.

The powerful digging ability of the mole lies in its sturdy fore-limbs, which are always turned outwards and have five strong, long claws. Moles dig permanent tunnels beneath the soil, with a central nest area lined with grass and leaves. There are occasional shafts up to the surface. Molehills are the earth thrown up on the surface from these shafts. Sometimes in damp soils a special sort of molehill, the fortress, is built to contain the central nesting-area. Tunnels may be up to 1 m deep, and usually the area in which one mole makes its tunnels does not overlap much with the territories of other moles. Moles live alone except in the mating

A mole is an expert miner. He constructs his own underground system

season, though they do seem to be aware of the presence of other moles nearby. Occasionally if there is a drought they are forced to leave their tunnel system and travel perhaps as far as 1 km to find water, a journey which may take them across the territories of up to 10 other moles. When one mole dies or is removed from its patch, its scent fades rapidly and the chemical warning telling other moles to keep away disappears. Other moles quickly take over the property. Sometimes one neighbour takes over the whole territory. Sometimes it is split up among several moles. There may be 5–25 moles per hectare of land, depending upon the soil quality, drainage and the availability of food. Moles outside the mating season are very unfriendly and fight furiously if they come across other moles.

A mole feeds on worms, slugs, beetles and insect larvae, most of which it finds as it patrols its tunnel system. If not enough food is available, the mole may dig some new tunnels. One adult animal can eat up to 50 gm of worms per day and it will store living worms (paralysed but not killed by having their heads bitten off) in a larder chamber near to the nest. This is done particularly in late autumn as a source of food during the winter.

Moles are active day and night. In

A rare sight! A mole above ground

A mole's skin is soft as velvet

winter both males and females work in the tunnels and sleep in their nests in 4-hour spells, which begin when they leave the nest around sunrise. Females do this all year round except in summer, when they are suckling their young and need to go back to the nest more often. During spring, males tend to sleep for short periods in their tunnels and spend much of the rest of their time looking for a mate. At this time they may not visit their nests for days on end. In summer they go back to the pattern of 4 hours' work, 4 hours' sleep, and then in autumn they become lazier and are active for only 2 periods of 4 hours a day. You might wonder how scientists have learnt all this about the mole's underground daily routine. The answer is that they have attached harmless radio transmitters to captured moles; the transmitters tell the scientists what the moles are doing once they have been set free again.

British moles mate between March and June. Surprisingly, since the mole lives underground, the breeding activity is controlled by the amount of daylight! We assume that the mole detects this when it comes to the surface, as it occasionally does when looking for nesting material, and that daylight acts as a signal to the mole's body that it is time to mate if a partner can be found. The young are born in litters of 2–7 after a pregnancy of 1 month. They are born naked but develop fur by the end of their second week of life. Their eyes open at the end of the third week and they suckle their mother's milk for a total of 4–6 weeks. Then they leave their mother's nest and wander off above ground in search of territory they can dig and claim for their own. It is at this time that large numbers (perhaps over half) of young moles are caught and killed by their enemies, including man. Moles are regarded as pests by gardeners and groundsmen, not only because of the damage molehills do to lawns and sports fields, but also because tunnelling by moles can harm the roots of young plants. Traps and poisons are used in attempts to kill moles.

A mole catcher

The Blackbird

Widespread and numerous in Great Britain, with even more migrating across the English Channel during the winter, this wonderful songbird (I vote it the best of native British songsters) is familiar to everyone. The male is easily recognizable – black with a yellow bill and a yellow ring around the eye. The female is perhaps less easily identified, being dark brown with a pale throat, dark bill and again a yellow ring around the eye. Young birds resemble the females but are generally paler and more mottled. Oddly enough, white blackbirds sometimes occur, though nearly all of these are only partly white, not true albinos (creatures lacking all colour).

Blackbirds are members of the thrush family, which includes 63 different species worldwide. They are intelligent birds that clearly regard the garden as their own and have little fear of human beings. They hop about the lawn and flowerbeds, stopping from time to time to cock their head and listen for the sound of worms moving underground. (They have very sharp hearing.) If they hear anything they will do a bit of digging, making shallow scrapes with their feet and pecking at the ground with their bill. They turn over leaves looking for insects and snails and search bushes and low trees for soft fruit. They tend to fly low, swerving

A male blackbird in typical pose

Blackbirds love berries

effortlessly round bushes and landing with tails held up and wings drooping.

Blackbirds are very territorial: they keep to what they consider their own plot of land, and chase other blackbirds off. So, if you have a pair of blackbirds in your garden, you will see a lot of them. If you have a garden pool or birdbath you will be able to see your blackbirds taking their daily bath and obviously enjoying it. A blackbird having a bath sits well down in the water, fluffing out its feathers, lifting and flapping its wings, flicking water over its back with its beak and then nibbling at its breast plumage. It's all done in quick fussy bursts, after which the bird flies off to its favourite spot for drying and preening – a branch or place on the fence close by. Shaking itself and fluffing up its feathers, the bird turns its head and prods with its beak at its preen gland, near the base of its tail. This gland contains waterproofing oil, which the prodding releases. The beak transfers the oil to the wing and body feathers, smearing them with a fine

The preen gland of a bird. It provides the oil for waterproofing

'Anting' – to keep down parasites

A female on her deep nest of grass and leaves

coating in a rapid series of nibbling movements.

In warm weather the blackbird will also do a bit of garden sunbathing, and, if there's a patch of sand or dust around, it will take the opportunity to have a dustbath, which keeps the feathers in good condition. You may also see a blackbird crouching with wings spread in a dry part of the garden allowing ants to run all over it. This apparently strange behaviour, called 'anting', is a form of pest control: the ants secrete an acid from glands at the rear of their abdomens and this kills off unwanted guests of the blackbird such as feather mites.

At breeding-time, blackbirds build a deep nest of grass and leaves, usually lightly cemented with mud and situated in a bush, climbing plant or garden shed. Nesting occurs earlier in gardens than in woodlands. The eggs, which are light blue-green with reddish speckles, are laid between March and July in 2 or 3 clutches of 3–6 eggs. The female incubates the eggs and the youngsters start to fly at about 2 weeks old.

The old nursery rhyme 'Sing a Song of Sixpence' mentions 'four and twenty blackbirds baked in a pie'. Many old nursery rhymes are like secret messages that you cannot understand unless you know the code, and this is true of 'Sing a Song of Sixpence'. It may refer to King Henry VIII, who in the sixteenth century decided to close down all the monasteries in England. The blackbirds may be the monasteries' choirs; the Queen in the parlour eating bread and honey may be Katherine of Aragon, Henry's first wife; and the maid hanging out the clothes may be Henry's second wife, Anne Boleyn.

A children's rhyme with a hidden meaning

The Ladybird

Not many people like insects, but then, most people think of insects as nasty creepy-crawlies. In fact there are some very beautiful insects, such as butterflies, dragonflies and scarab beetles (which come from the East and have shells so lovely that they have been used as jewellery). These are the sort of insects nearly everyone likes, though few realize that they are insects. The same is true of the beetle called the ladybird. The 'lady' in its name refers to the Virgin Mary ('Our Lady') and the 'bird' here just means a flying creature.

If a ladybird lands on you, then according to an old English tradition you are supposed not to flick it off but to blow gently and say,

> Ladybird, ladybird, fly away home.
> Your house is on fire and your
> children are gone.

It is thought that this verse refers to the old practice of setting fire to hop fields in September after the harvest.

In Northumberland in the north of England, where an old name for the ladybird is the 'reed sodger', there is a similar tradition. You throw the ladybird into the air and say,

> Reed, reed sodger fly away
> And make the morn a sunny day.

French children recite a verse that warns the ladybird of a Turkish invasion and the slaughter of all her young ones. Everywhere the ladybird is regarded as a good and useful creature, feeding as it does on both the larvae and adult forms of aphids – pests such as the greenfly. The number of spots on a ladybird's wings was thought to indicate

A seven-spot out and about

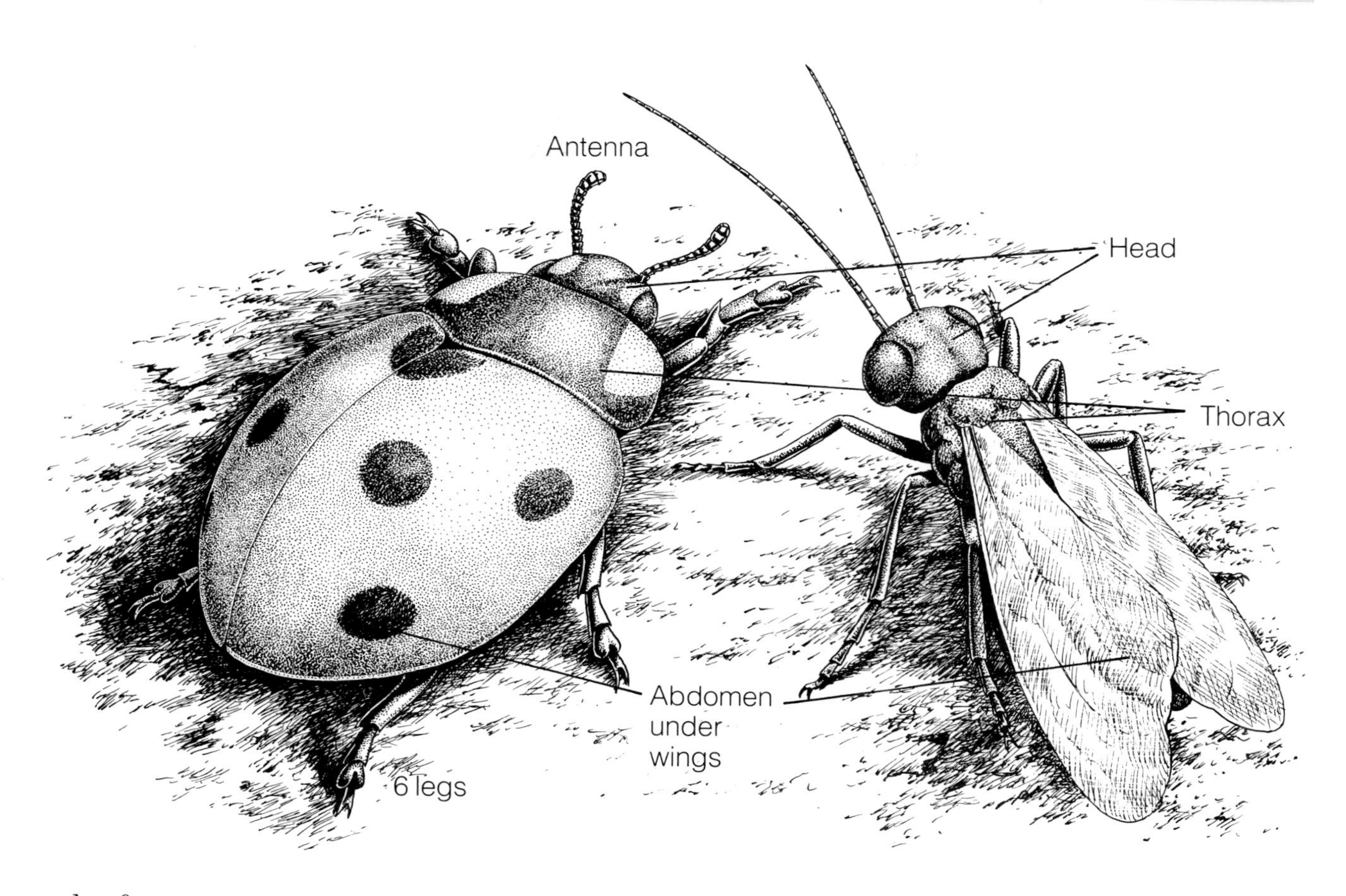

The basic insect body and a ladybird compared. The ladybird uses one pair of wings as a wing-case

the future price of wheat: each spot represented an extra shilling for a bushel of corn (5 pence for 36 litres). It was considered particularly unlucky to kill a ladybird, and in East Anglia, for example, if one were accidentally killed it would be carefully buried and the grave stamped upon 3 times while the rhyme 'Ladybird, ladybird, fly away home' was recited. At one time the yellow liquid which the insect secretes when alarmed was considered an effective treatment for toothache. The sufferer rubbed his finger on the ladybird's legs and then rubbed the liquid onto the aching tooth.

Like other insects, ladybirds are creatures that live on land, have no backbones or lungs, and breathe through a system of simple air-tubes that open onto the body surface. The body is divided into three main parts the head, the chest or thorax, and the abdomen. It is covered by a horny coating or external skeleton which is shed now and again to allow the insect to grow. The head carries a pair of feelers or antennae and there are three pairs of feeding appendages. Generally there are one or two pairs of wings arising from the thorax and three pairs of legs.

True beetles, of which there are around 300,000 species, form the biggest group of insects, and range in size from 0.5 mm to over 15 cm long. The largest are the *Goliath beetles*, which are some of the biggest insects alive. The Latin name (*Coleoptera*) of the beetle family means 'sheath wings' and refers to the fore-wings, which form an armoured covering for the delicate hind wings used for flying. Beetles live mainly on the ground and have a heavily armoured head with a mouth formed for biting and compound eyes, which allow the beetle

The ladybird is a carnivore, not a plant-eater

to see almost all the way round itself.

There are 400 species of ladybird in the world and there are 41 species in Great Britain. All are round in outline with hemispherical bodies (like an up-turned pudding bowl) where the head is concealed beneath the thorax. Most are brightly coloured and spotted. They have short and nimble legs. Nearly all are carnivorous, which means that they eat other animals. Ladybirds are indeed gardeners' friends, though there are a few exceptions: for instance, the squash ladybird of the United States damages pumpkins. The striking colours and designs of ladybirds serve to warn creatures that might be tempted to eat them that they contain poisonous chemicals, though no human can be harmed by handling them.

If you look carefully you may be able to identify 5 or 6 different species of ladybird busily going about their business of keeping down the greenfly in your garden. One of the commonest is the *seven-spot ladybird*, which is about 6 mm long and has 3 black spots on each of its bright red wing-cases, with the seventh spot shared between them. You will often find this ladybird resting under a flower-head. A plant it is particularly fond of is hogweed. The biggest ladybird in Britain is the *eyed ladybird*, about 8 mm long. It is frequently found on pine-trees and displays 7 or 8 spots on each wing-case. The most common British ladybird is the *two-spot*. Generally it has one spot on each wing-case, but just to confuse you it may have a total of 4 or even 6! Some varieties reverse the colouring by having red spots on black wing-cases. The *ten-spot ladybird* is also quite common and tends to favour woodland. It possesses red, brown or black wing-cases with yellow, black or orange spots. It is about 4 mm long and has tiny yellow legs. In southern parts of England the *fourteen-spot ladybird* can sometimes be found. It is about 4 mm long and has very bright and distinct yellow and black markings. Smaller still at 3 mm long is the *twenty-two spot ladybird*, which has 11 black spots on each yellow or pale orange wing-case. It can be found in certain areas of England, Wales and eastern Ireland.

A twenty-two spot ladybird

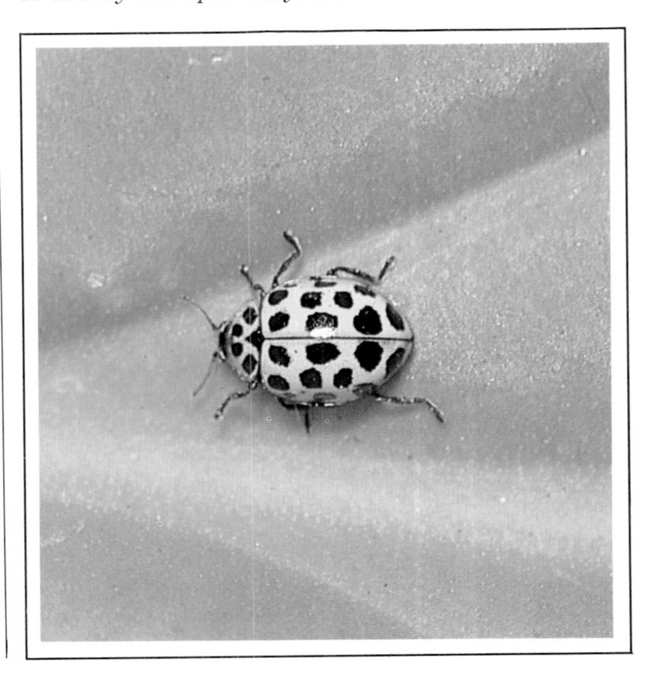

A fourteen-spot ladybird with spots fused together

The *twenty-four spot ladybird* is an interesting creature, being a vegetarian that feeds on clover and similar plants. Despite its name, it has a total of 16–20 irregularly sized spots on its orange wing-cases. It is another of the smaller ladybirds, at around 3 mm long.

Although ladybirds tend to remain calm with their wing-cases closed when you pick one up or gently touch one sitting on a flower, they are very good at flying. Their finely veined transparent hind wings can carry them over vast distances. Some ladybirds migrate to Britain from continental Europe and occasionally a swarm of them can number tens of thousands. If they are unlucky enough to meet with bad weather on the way, so many of them may fall into the sea that the water seems to turn red.

Adult ladybirds hibernate over winter in Great Britain. Look for them beneath pieces of loose bark or on the underside of dry and sheltered window-sills. Many die of diseases such as fungus infections. They also have an enemy in the form of a wasp-like insect that lays its eggs within the body of the adult ladybird. When the eggs hatch into grubs they feed on the flesh of the ladybird but do not necessarily kill it. Sometimes you will see the tiny pupa of the parasite still attached to a ladybird as it works its way along a stem full of greenfly.

Each female ladybird lays about 200 eggs, generally on the underside of leaves and conveniently near to greenfly colonies. Larvae emerge from the eggs and begin feeding on the aphids, killing perhaps 30 or 40 every day. The larval ladybird, a slate-blue caterpillar-like creature with yellow spots, grows to be much longer than the adult beetle at around 12–13 mm. In the 3 weeks before the larva turns into a pupa it eats it way through many hundreds of aphids. At the end of the 3 weeks the larva shrinks and rounds off into a hard-cased grey and yellow oval pupa, rather like a button. The pupa is firmly attached to a stem of leaf, generally in an exposed position, and stays there until the adult ladybird emerges from it.

The baby is longer than the adult!

The Centipede and Millipede

Do a bit of digging and you will soon enough come across a flattish, rusty-brown, many-legged creature that wriggles artfully away from your trowel or spade. It is the centipede, and, like the ladybird, it is a friend of the gardener. Centipedes are not insects – though, funnily enough, they are more closely related to insects than to the somewhat similar millipedes. There are around 3000 species of centipede. Almost all of them live on the land and have elongated bodies made up of many segments, with a distinct head, one pair of feelers or antennae, and a single pair of legs on each segment. As most species are carnivorous, preying upon small animals such as slugs and insects, they help to control plant pests in the garden. Like insects, spiders and Crustaceans (such as lobsters and crabs) centipedes have their skeletons on the outside of the body in the form of a tough outer shell or 'exoskeleton'. This cannot stretch, so the centipede has to shed its body covering from time to time to be able to grow. The cast-off outer skeletons are whitish and hollow, and look rather 'ghostly'. You may be able to find them lying in the garden.

Although the word 'centipede' means 'a hundred feet', the number of feet varies from 34 to 254, depending on the species. The longest known species is a 46-legged giant living in the jungles of South America, which when fully grown is about 40 cm long but can reach 90 cm! Big centipedes such as this are fully grown at around 4 years old and may live for 10 years. British centipedes, of which there are 44 species, don't get

The centipede is blind as a bat

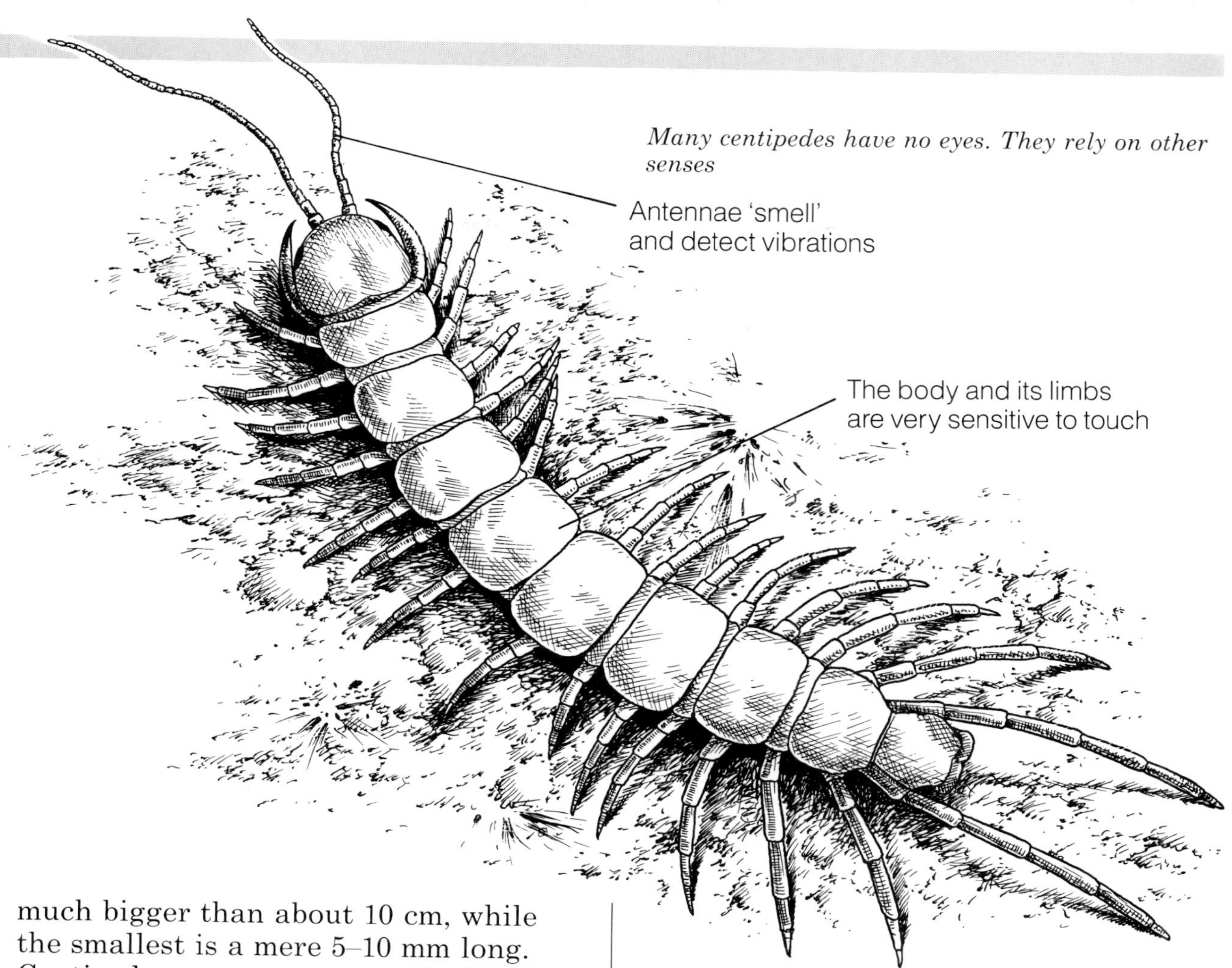

Many centipedes have no eyes. They rely on other senses

much bigger than about 10 cm, while the smallest is a mere 5–10 mm long. Centipedes seem to move quite fast, but probably no species can leg it at more than 5 miles (8 km) per hour. The first pair of legs on a centipede are not used for walking but have been modified into poison fangs. These are used to paralyse and kill prey. Though most centipedes are harmless to human beings, there are a few foreign species now resident in Britain which can give a most unpleasant nip.

Centipedes are nocturnal. Sunlight and heat are lethal to them. Unlike insects, they do not have within their outer skin a waxy waterproof layer that retains body moisture. A few hours of exposure to dry or sunny conditions will kill a centipede. This is why you will often find dead centipedes in greenhouses or under sheets of glass. The world of the centipede is one of complete darkness. None of the British species has any form of eye. To catch their prey, centipedes rely on their highly developed sense of touch, their ability to pick up vibrations and the chemical detecting-cells in their antennae. Although most centipedes feed only on other creatures, such as woodlice, slugs, insects and smaller centipedes, there is one species at least that can damage growing celery and lettuce.

Female centipedes lay eggs one at a time. The egg is then handled by special claws at the back of the body and is smeared with a special sticky liquid to which bits of soil cling, making it hard to see. The egg is then hidden in the earth or under leaf mould and another egg is laid. From the eggs tiny but perfectly formed baby centipedes with fewer legs than the adult eventually emerge.

Keep your eyes open and you may be

able to recognize several different kinds of centipede in your garden. The *common centipede* is around 3 cm long, possesses 60 legs and holds its body rigid when running. (Most other species move with a snaky side-to-side movement.) During the day this centipede is often found beneath stones or bits of wood. Another common species, *Halophilus*, is up to 7 cm long, thin and yellowish, with 160 or more legs. *Necrophloephagus* is a yellowish centipede with a dark brown head. It is about 3.5 cm long and often burrows in gardens.

The centipede should not be confused with another multi-legged creature of the garden, the millipede. The name 'millipede' means 'a thousand feet', but no millipede has anything like that

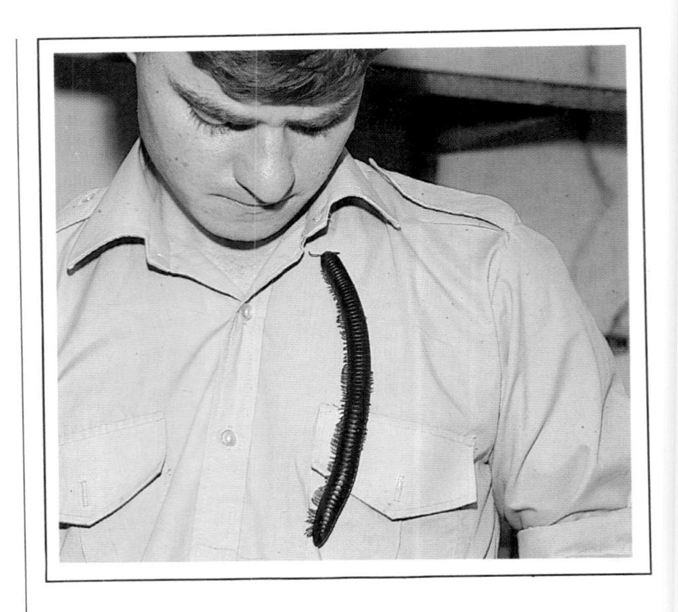

Giant millipedes make harmless pets

Millipedes don't have a thousand legs!

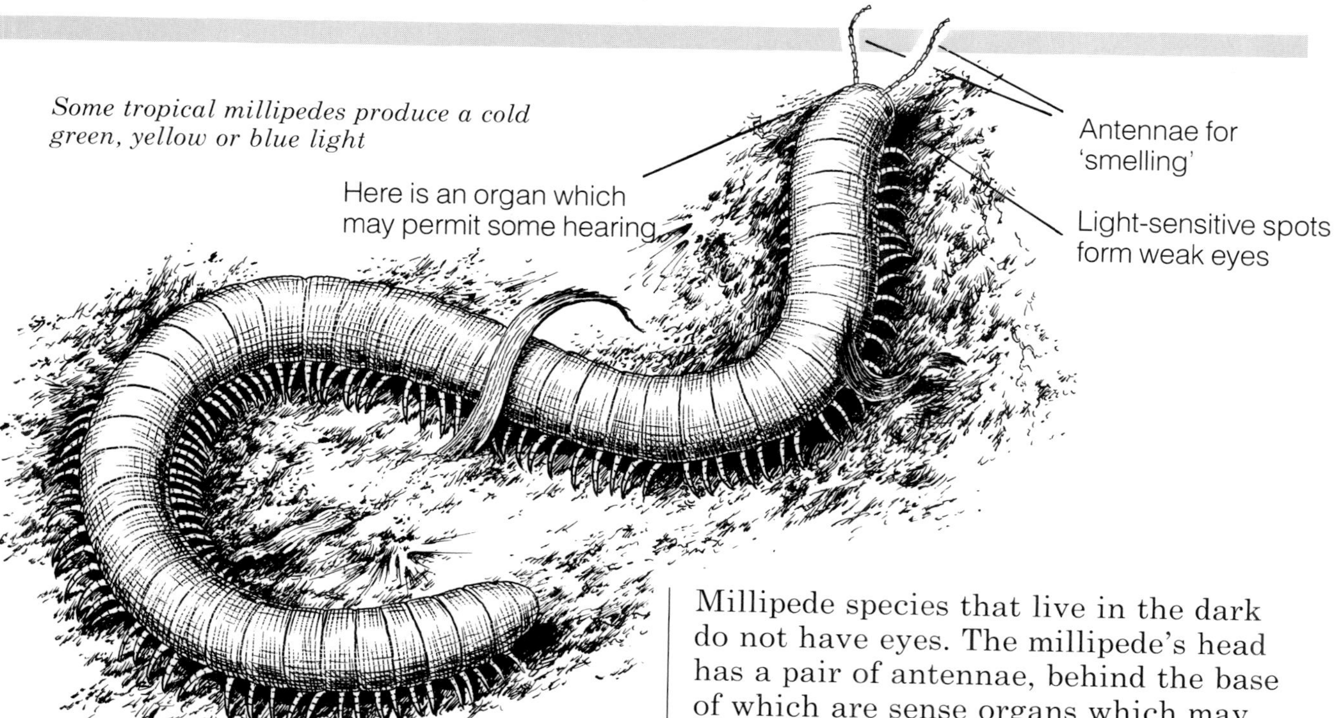

Some tropical millipedes produce a cold green, yellow or blue light

number of feet! Unlike centipedes, millipedes are almost wholly vegetarian, and, whereas centipedes have one pair of legs on each segment, millipedes boast two pairs. Like centipedes, millipedes live in the soil and under leaf mould. The tiniest are only 2 mm long, but the biggest (which come from the tropics and make excellent cheap exotic pets) can reach 20 cm.

50 species of millipede live in the United Kingdom. One of the commonest is the *black snake millipede*, which grows up to 30 mm long and has 96 pairs of legs. When it is attacked it curls itself up into a flat coil so that its strong exoskeleton can protect its softer under-belly. As it rolls up it secretes a smelly poisonous liquid from a line of glands along the side of its body. This puts off most attackers. Another common British millipede is the *pill millipede* (about 50 mm long), which has a shiny body with broad back and narrow yellow bands. When threatened, it curls itself up into a little ball.

Most species of millipede have eyes, but these, unlike the powerful eyes of insects, are simply light-sensitive spots. Millipede species that live in the dark do not have eyes. The millipede's head has a pair of antennae, behind the base of which are sense organs which may give the creature some hearing ability. Use a magnifying glass to look at the legs and movement of a millipede. The legs possess 6 or 7 joints and in most species arise close together along the middle of the under-surface. Millipedes do not move quickly but they are certainly graceful, crawling along with lovely wavy movements.

Female millipedes lay eggs from which larvae looking like miniature versions of the adults but with a smaller number of body segments and legs emerge. As the larva grows, new segments develop.

Amazingly, many foreign kinds of millipede can produce light! On the undersurface of their bodies are two kinds of glands. When mixed, the liquid secreted by these glands undergoes a remarkable chemical change, producing bluish, yellowish or greenish light. This light, which was recorded by Christopher Columbus and his companions when they visited Santo Domingo on their first voyage to the New World, has nothing to do with producing heat. It is similar to the light emitted by other kinds of living creature, such as fire-flies. It is a pity that no British variety of millipede shares this ability.

The Butterfly

Butterflies are short-lived but beautiful inhabitants of the summer garden. Despite their name, they have nothing to do with butter! The way in which the butterfly emerges from the husk that was its chrysalis or pupa is rather like something that was dead coming to life, and this is why it reminded people of the idea that when someone dies the 'soul' leaves the body and lives on. Butterflies were even thought of as the carriers of souls.

Moths are similar to butterflies and belong to the same group of insects, *Lepidoptera*; but there are some important differences between them. First, butterflies are active by day, while most moths are more active at night. Secondly, resting moths usually hold their wings spread out, while resting butterflies hold them pressed together. Thirdly, the feelers or antennae of butterflies are slender with blobs on the tips, while those of moths are short and feathery.

Butterflies are true insects and their bodies possess all the basic features of insects, with a body divided into 3 parts: head, thorax (chest) and abdomen, which has 11 rather indistinct segments. 6 legs arise from the thorax and each segment of the abdomen possesses a pair of air-tubes or spiracles opening onto the skin surface, through which the creature breathes. And, of course, they have wings. But there are many special features about butterflies which make them not only the most beautiful but also some of the cleverest creatures in your garden.

In the first place, butterflies have the keenest sense of smell in the animal kingdom. Each antenna has 40,000 tiny receptors linked to nerves for handling general smells. A male butterfly can pick up the scent of a female from as far away as 11 km, yet the total stock of perfume carried by a female is no more than 0.0001 mg! It appears that, when he has picked up the scent of a female, the male starts flying into the wind, which has carried the smell. To help him find his way, he has instruments that

The life-cycle of a butterfly

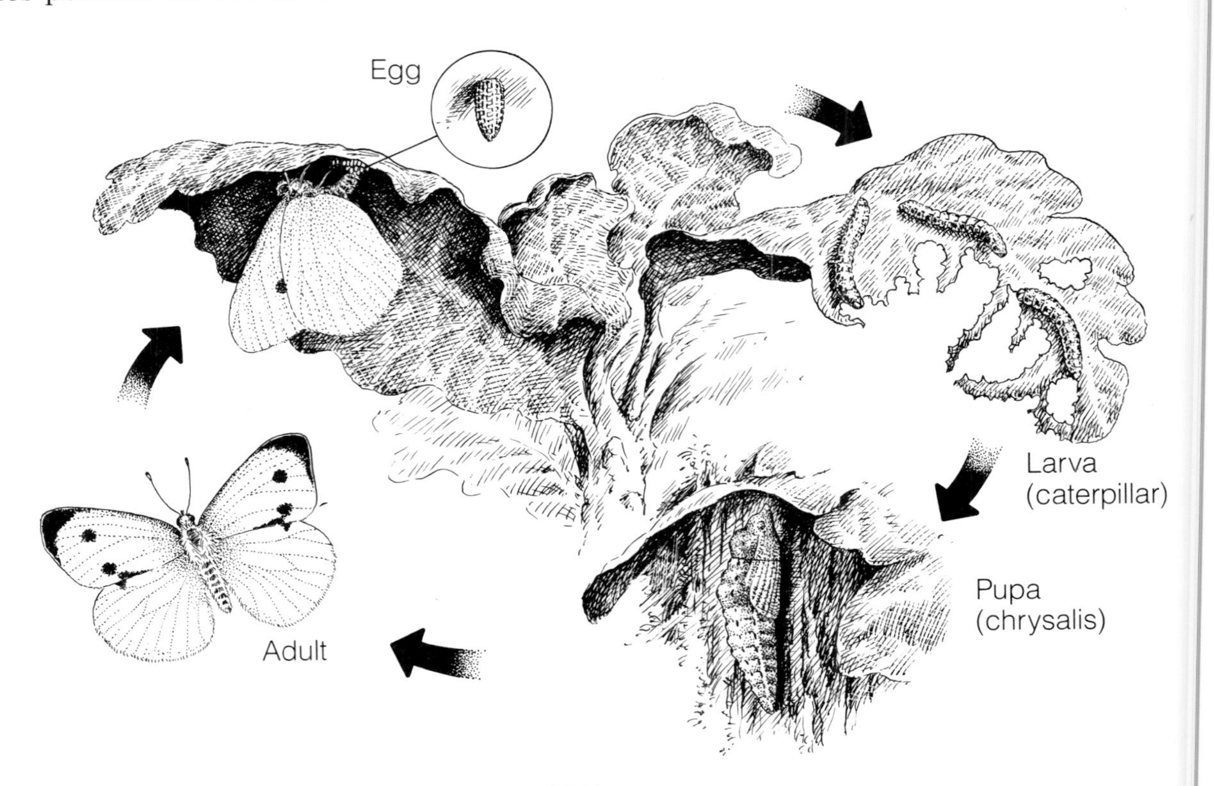

measure the wind located in joints of his antennae. So that he doesn't miss the female's scent among all the other smells in the air, the male has special receptor cells that react only to the perfume of the female.

Butterflies have 2 compound eyes, like a lot of eyes joined together. They

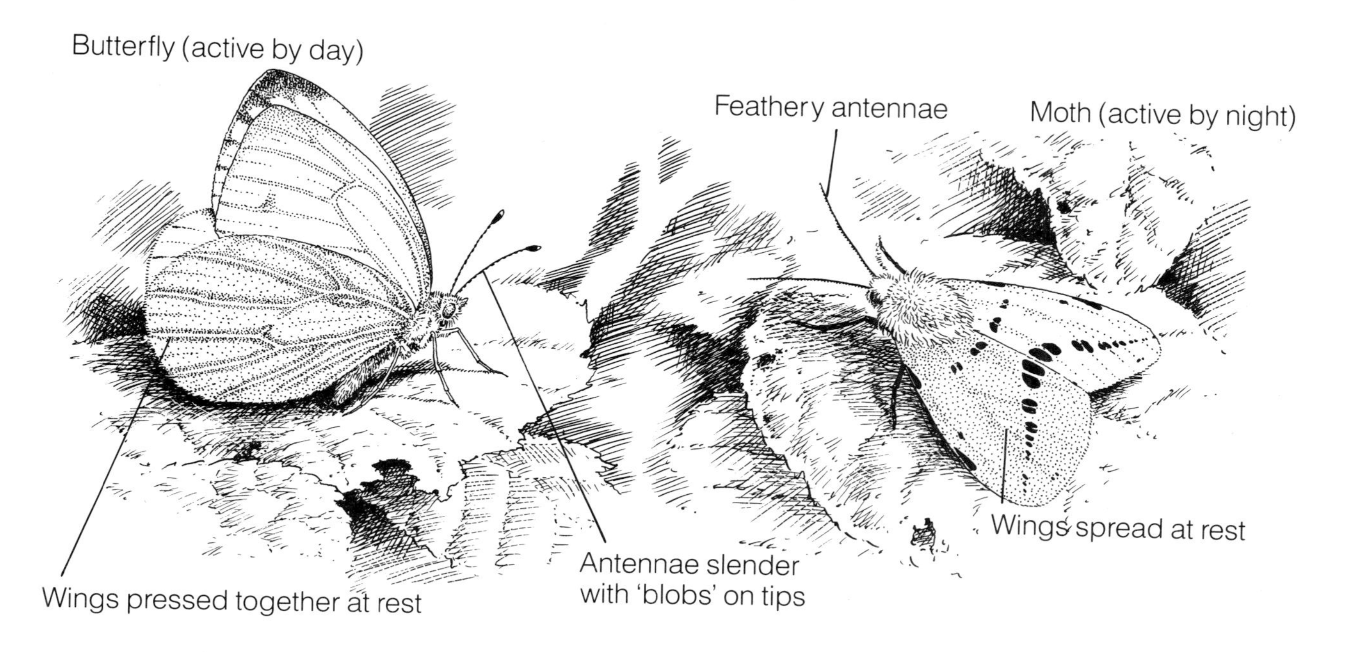

are particularly good at receiving red colours, which is important for the pollination of plants such as the Sweet William. Unlike the human eye, the eye of the butterfly is sensitive to ultraviolet light, which allows it to see colours we can't. If a plant reflects ultraviolet light, its colour for a butterfly will be quite different from its colour for us. For instance, the red poppy reflects ultraviolet light, so to a butterfly it is not red at all but a pure ultraviolet, a sort of deep blue.

The glory of both butterflies and moths is, of course, their wings. Their family name, *Lepidoptera*, means 'scale-wings'. If you handle a butterfly gently, you will find your fingers quickly covered with a fine powder that dusts off the wings. Look at the powder under a microscope and you will see that it is made up of beautifully formed little scales. These scales are pegged to the wing like tiles on a roof. Some butterfly wings, particularly in the tropics, shimmer with blue light. This is caused by grooves on the scales, which absorb all colours in the light except blue. Butterflies are very good at flying: some species migrate, and they can travel as

Differences between moth and butterfly

Sense of direction and smell are superb

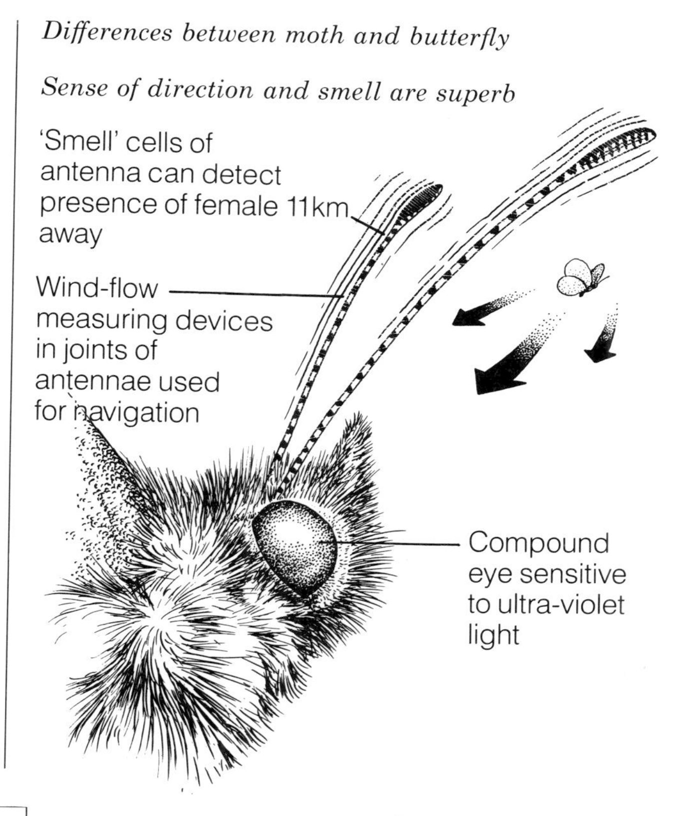

far as 3000 km.

Look at the head of a butterfly. At the front of the head is a 'tongue' that when not in use is coiled like a watch-spring. Actually this is a tube that when stretched right out is used to suck nectar from flowers. Almost all butterflies (and moths) feed upon nectar.

Silver studded blues

Occasionally the juices of over-ripe fruit are also taken, particularly by species such as the *red admiral*. One of Britain's rarest and most spectacular butterflies, the *purple emperor*, likes to suck the juices of the rotting bodies of animals.

If you wish to attract butterflies to your garden, you must avoid using sprays that kill insects and weeds. A bank of mixed flowers in a border is very appealing to butterflies, especially if behind it there is a brick wall that heats up in the sun. Different flowers appeal to different butterflies, so, the more varieties you have, the more different types of butterfly you are likely to see. If you can, it is a very good idea to have a patch of wild flowers.

The eggs of butterflies come in various shapes and the designs on their shells can be unbelievably beautiful, but you must look at them under a microscope to see them properly. Some females may lay a thousand or more eggs. The eggs are laid on a plant that the caterpillars can eat after they hatch. Their first meal on hatching, though, is the shell of the egg, which contains vitamins essential to the health of the caterpillars. Only one in every hundred butterfly eggs get to the point of hatching. The rest perish from disease or are eaten by birds, bugs, mites or certain flies. It usually takes 1–2 weeks for the eggs to hatch.

Caterpillars have 3 pairs of true legs attached to the thorax or chest and 5 pairs of temporary legs attached to the abdomen. The legs have hooks or claws for grasping leaves and twigs. The head has powerful cutting jaws, a pair of very short feelers or antennae, and 6 simple light-spot eyes on each side. Along the sides of the body are 9 pairs of small dots: these are breathing holes or spiracles. Beneath the mouth is an opening that leads from the glands that

The beautiful eggs of the small white

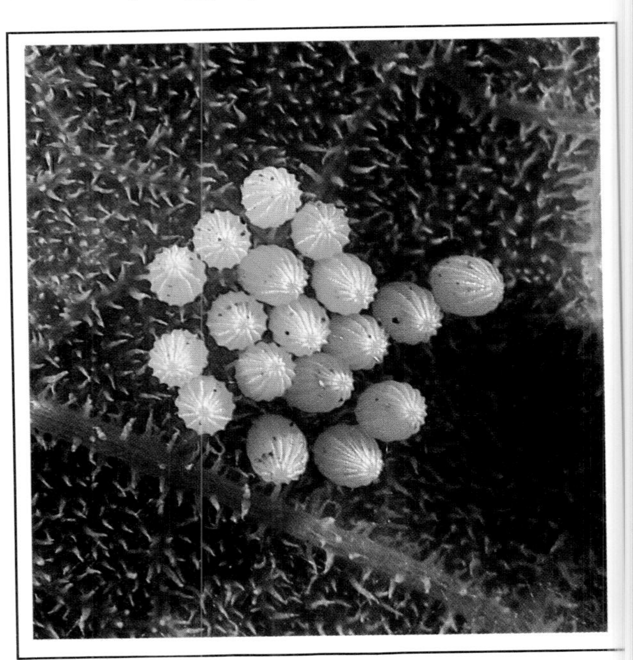

Peacock caterpillars on nettles in June

make silk, which is used to make and fix the cocoons in which the pupa or chrysalis changes into a butterfly.

Caterpillars protect themselves from enemies in a whole variety of ways. Some are hairy, some are armed with spikes and spines, and in some tropical varieties the spines are attached to poison glands and can sting. Some caterpillars protect themselves by feeding only at night; others form cases or webs on the leaves. Some hide themselves by having the same pattern or colour as the plant they feed upon. Even so, 99 per cent of caterpillars are eaten by birds and other creatures or die from disease.

As caterpillars grow, they moult their tough skins 4 times. The new skin is soft and stretches, but it soon hardens into a exoskeleton. After the fourth moult the caterpillar changes into a pupa or chrysalis. Some pupae are enclosed in a covering or cocoon of silk, while others are simply glued to a plant or hang from a silken pad. The pupa is a hard casing formed from the skin of a caterpillar with the legs glued down into it. Many sorts of chrysalis look like dead leaves or bits of dried stem, to protect them. Within the chrysalis the caterpillar gradually turns into an adult butterfly, and when it is ready the insect breaks out of the chrysalis, pumps liquid into the veins of its wings to stretch them out, and sits for up to 2 hours waiting for them to dry. Then for the first time, it soars into the air, the brand-new wings beating at up to 10 times per second.

The biggest living butterfly is the female *Queen Alexandra birdwing* of New Guinea, which has a wingspan of almost 30 cm! The biggest native British butterfly is the *swallowtail* (7–10 cm), and the smallest is the *small blue* (2–2.5 cm). If you are a real butterfly fan, the best place to go is Brazil, where there are hundreds of species, but there is still plenty of variety in Britain, with 70

The cabbage white

recorded species. Here are some of them, divided into groups by colour.

The *whites* include such species as the *small white*, *wood white*, *green-veined white* and the *orange tip*. The most familiar and notorious is the *large cabbage white*, whose caterpillars eat cabbages and other plants. There are 2 generations of large cabbage white in Britain each year, the first between April and June and the second between July and September.
There are several species of *yellow* butterfly, but the one you are most likely to see is the *brimstone*. This is a truly butter-coloured butterfly, and some people believe that it is how the

The brimstone butterfly

butterfly got its name.
All the *brown* butterflies have false 'eye' designs on the upper or lower surfaces of their wings to deter their enemies. The commonest British butterfly is the *meadow brown*. It lives for 1 month and

The meadow brown. Note the 'eyes'

flies on dull and even rainy days.
Some of the *blue* butterflies are very rare, but the one you are most likely to see in the garden is the *common blue*.

A large skipper

There are 8 species of British *skipper*. These are small, yellow-brownish butterflies, frequently with white markings. They are fast and quite aggressive, and will chase off other flying insects, including bees.

The gorgeous comma

The *comma* loves buddleias, asters and Michaelmas daisies. With its wings folded, the adult looks like a dead and ragged leaf.

A red admiral on buddleia flowers

The *red admiral* flies by night as well as day. It often rests and sunbathes, spreading and displaying its gorgeous wings. It delights in feeding on ice-plants, buddleias and Michaelmas daisies in the autumn.

A summer visitor: the painted lady

The *painted lady* migrates to Britain from Southern Europe and North Africa in May and June. It is very fond of garden flowers and thistles, but cannot survive the British winter.
The *fritillaries* are orange or brown butterflies with black spots. They prefer woodlands to gardens.
The *peacock* likes stinging nettles, and you should look for its black, hairy caterpillars on these plants in June. The adult enjoys feeding on the sap of ripe fruit in orchards. It gets its name from the eyes on its wings, which are intended to 'stare' at and frighten away enemies.

The glamorous peacock butterfly

The Bee

The bee is the royal emblem of France. Yes, it is true that the emblem is called the fleur-de-lis, which is French for the iris, but this shape was originally meant to represent a flying bee. The old royal robe and banners of France were thickly sewn

The fleur-de-lis: not a plant, but a bee

with golden bees, and when the tomb of the early French king Childeric (436–81 AD) was opened in the seventeenth century it was found to contain 300 bees made of gold.

People like bees because they make honey and pollinate flowers. Everybody knows that they are very busy creatures, and you will often see them working in your garden. Some species, such as the *honey bee*, live in well-organized colonies or hives. These bees are called 'social' bees, and the females are of 2 types: there are a few 'queen' bees, who can lay eggs, and lots and lots of 'worker' bees, who cannot breed at all. The males are called 'drones'. You may be surprised to learn that most species of bee are 'solitary' bees: they live on their own, and the female makes a nest for her 'brood', the larvae that hatch from the eggs she lays.

Bees are insects and have hairy, plump bodies which are large compared with their wings. The joints of the hind legs are specially big and covered with thick hair, which collects pollen. The eggs of bees are laid singly in chambers or cells, and each bee's nest contains a number of cells; the hive bee's has many thousands. Along with each egg enough food is deposited to feed the larva until it turns into a pupa. Adult bees feed on nectar and pollen from flowers. The larvae also eat pollen and honey, which is made from nectar in the bee's 'honey

The body of the bee

stomach' and then brought up again at the nest or hive. Honey is a form of concentrated nectar rich in sugars. Pollen contains lots of protein.

Solitary bees make their nests in a variety of places. Some make burrows in the ground, with single cells leading off a main passage. Others make use of spaces they find in buildings, walls, trees or bushes. They may even use keyholes or empty snail shells!

Honey bees build the cells of the hive out of scales of wax, which they produce from glands on the under-surface of their abdomens. They shape the wax by lifting it on their legs and kneading it with their jaws. To seal cracks in the honeycomb, bees like to collect resin from trees. If there are no trees available, they may fetch warm tar from a nearby road. To soften the wax of the honeycomb, water is needed, and every day some bees will go in search of ponds and puddles. The cells are built very carefully. The bee measures everything it does using its antennae and the sensitive bristles on its abdomen. If the honeycomb is damaged, the bees at once start making repairs.

The bee that you see in the garden is a living machine far more complex than any rocket or computer. Bees have a perfect sense of temperature and can detect rises or falls of less than 1°C. Temperature control is very important to honey bees, and they have worked out ways of keeping a constant temperature of 35°C in the hive's breeding-cells. In cool weather, worker bees crowd together in their thousands on top of the cells to warm them up. If it goes colder, they huddle closer and cover the brood cells with their bodies to make a living eiderdown. On the other hand, if it is too hot they bring in water and cover the combs with a fine film which they then cause to evaporate by fanning it with their wings. They sit like little ventilators over the cells driving the warm air towards each other and pushing it out again through the entrance.

A typical beehive

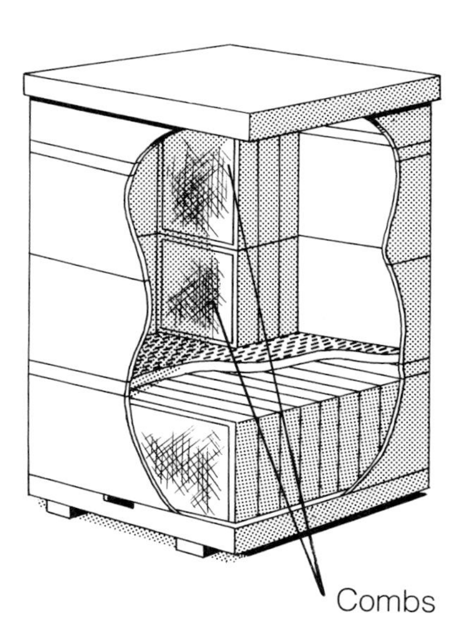

A bee-keeper inspects a honeycomb

The compound eye of the bee is made up of 15,000 parts or facets, which are like lots of separate eyes and divide everything the bee sees into a screen of squares. It uses this screen in order to find its way and work out its speed. As the bee flies along, it charts its course in relation to the sun and the way in which what it sees changes on its screen tells it how fast it is flying.

The bee also has a mechanism that works out air-speed. This is centred in nerves within the joints of the antennae. When the wind bends the antennae, signals are sent into the central computer. By comparing the signals from the antennae with the information from the eye about the bee's flying-speed, the computer works out at once the angle at which the bee should fly. What is more, the eyeball of a bee has rows of tiny hairs where the facets join. These hairs sense air-movements, and in next to no time the bee can correct its flight when it is affected by gusts of wind, so that it is not blown off-course.

In the hairy fur between the bee's compound eyes are 3 tiny eye spots, which are used to measure how light it is (like the lightmeter on a camera). These light meters are very important, because they tell a bee when it is safe to go out in the morning and also when it should return home. The bee's computer tells it how far it is from the hive or nest, and as the light fades the bee can tell when it must leave for home and how fast it must fly to reach there at the right time.

The bee's two antennae have nerve receptors which react to the level of carbon dioxide in the air. If the amount rises, it immediately triggers off a rapid fanning motion of the wings. This mechanism is employed by worker bees to ensure that the air in the hive is always fresh. The chemical receptors of the antennae can also pick up the scents of blossoms, and, depending on which antenna picks up the stronger scent, the bee knows which way to fly to find the flowers producing the scent. (If both antennae give the same message, the bee is heading in the right direction.) The antennae are not the only way in which bees seek out food flowers. They use their eyes too, and because they (like butterflies) can see ultra-violet light, they see things in a completely different way from us. One colour they cannot see is red, which looks black to them. But, because some flowers that look red to us reflect ultra-violet light, the bee sees them as a deep blue!

Bees cannot hear in the same way as we can, but they can pick up vibrations through the soles of their feet and use vibrations to 'speak' to other bees.

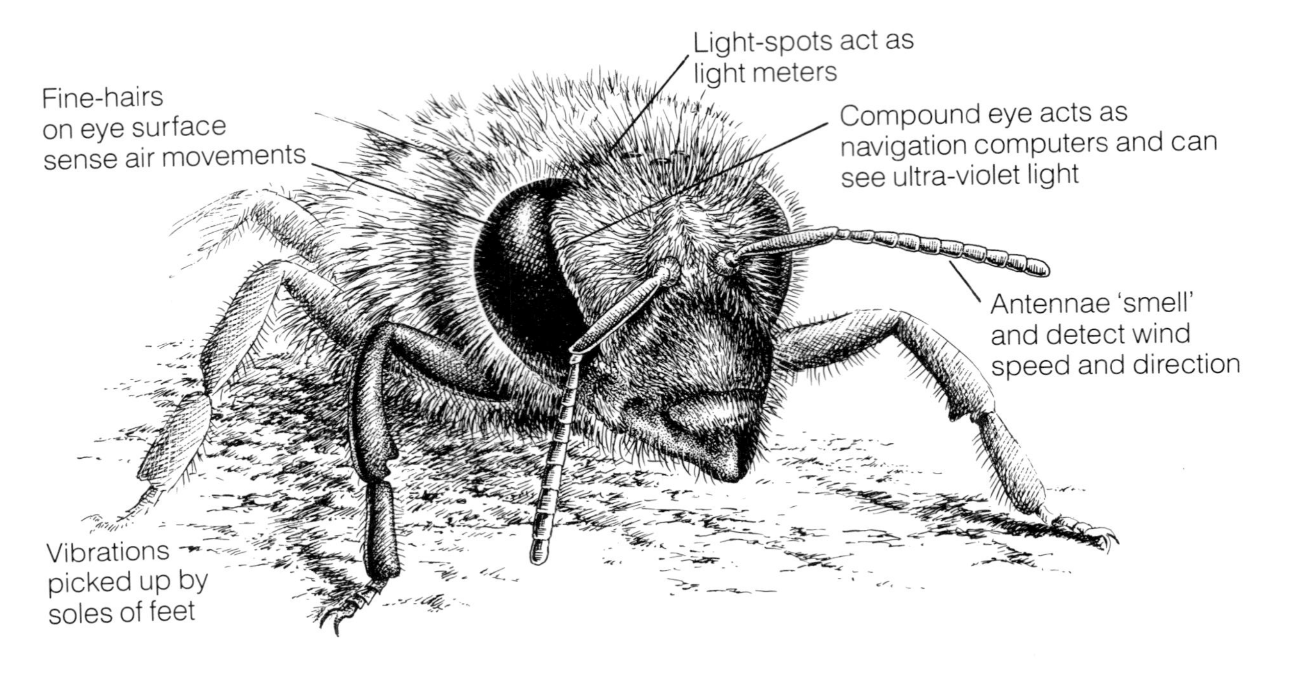

A bee's senses are truly amazing

Bees swarming on a tree trunk

Another way in which bees can communicate with each other is through dancing! The other bees watch the dance and get the message at once.

You may one day see bees swarm in your garden. This happens when there are too many bees in a colony. The colony prepares to divide by swarming. Dense balls containing thousands of bees form a swarm and they tend to occur between May and July. You might see them attached to the branch of a tree as a sort of buzzing ball, and sometimes they will build a temporary honeycomb there before setting up the new colony. If bees do swarm in your garden, don't be frightened but leave the bees alone. You should ask a local beekeeper for advice. He may move the swarm, which has to be done very carefully.

Despite all their skills and industry, most bees do not live very long. Honey bees live for only about 1 month in summer. Lots of people think that all the bees they see in the garden are honey bees, but in fact there are over 200 different species of bee in Britain and the honey bee is only one of them. *Bumble bees*, of which there are 18 species in Britain, are easily recognized because of their big furry bodies. Like honey bees, they are social bees. Each colony has one queen, plus lots of female workers and male drones.

Everyone knows that bees can sting. The sting is a sort of poison needle that sticks out from the end of the abdomen. Worker bees use it as a means of defence and always die after stinging, as the sting is barbed (like an arrow) and cannot be pulled out when it has been used. Queen bees that have not bred and laid eggs have unbarbed stings, used for killing other queens.

A honey bee at work

The same flower visited by a bumble bee

The Frog

To me frogs and toads are fascinating animals. They are quiet, neat, slightly comical creatures and they live in ponds. You often see frogs in your garden, even if there is no pond or pool but just some damp and shady areas.

Frogs are amphibians – creatures that live both on land and in water – but unlike reptiles (such as snakes) they have naked, moist skin which is used in breathing to obtain oxygen. Most young amphibians hatch from eggs that are deposited in water and develop into larvae that breathe through external gills in a similar way to fish. They gradually change into animals that can live on land. Their gills disappear and they begin to breathe through their skin and a brand-new pair of lungs.

There are 1800 species of frog and toad in the world today. The biggest frog in the world is the rare *Goliath frog* from Guinea in West Africa. The biggest frog in Britain is the *marsh frog*, which arrived from Hungary in 1935. From the tip of its nose to the base of its rump it measures 10–13 cm, while the biggest native frog, the *common frog*, doesn't quite reach 10 cm.

A frog at home

The common toad

Although some toads are long-lived and can perhaps reach 40 years of age, frogs tend not to live anywhere near as long. There may be exceptions (we don't know much about the Goliath frog, for instance), but the limit for the species we know a lot about seems to be about 16 years.

If you pick up a frog, hold it very gently and look at it carefully. Don't keep it in your warm hands for more than a minute or two – such a cool and damp-skinned animal finds it most uncomfortable! The frog has a special kind of tongue which is fixed to the front of the mouth and can be flicked forward. Within the tongue are lots of glands which ooze and make it sticky. When a frog sees an insect, it flicks out its tongue, which sticks to the insect and pulls it back into the frog's mouth. Although adult frogs are carnivores, their larvae (tadpoles) are vegetarians when first hatched and feed on algae, which are tiny plants that grow in water.

Watch a frog sitting quietly, gulping from time to time as its throat pumps up and down. What it is doing is breathing

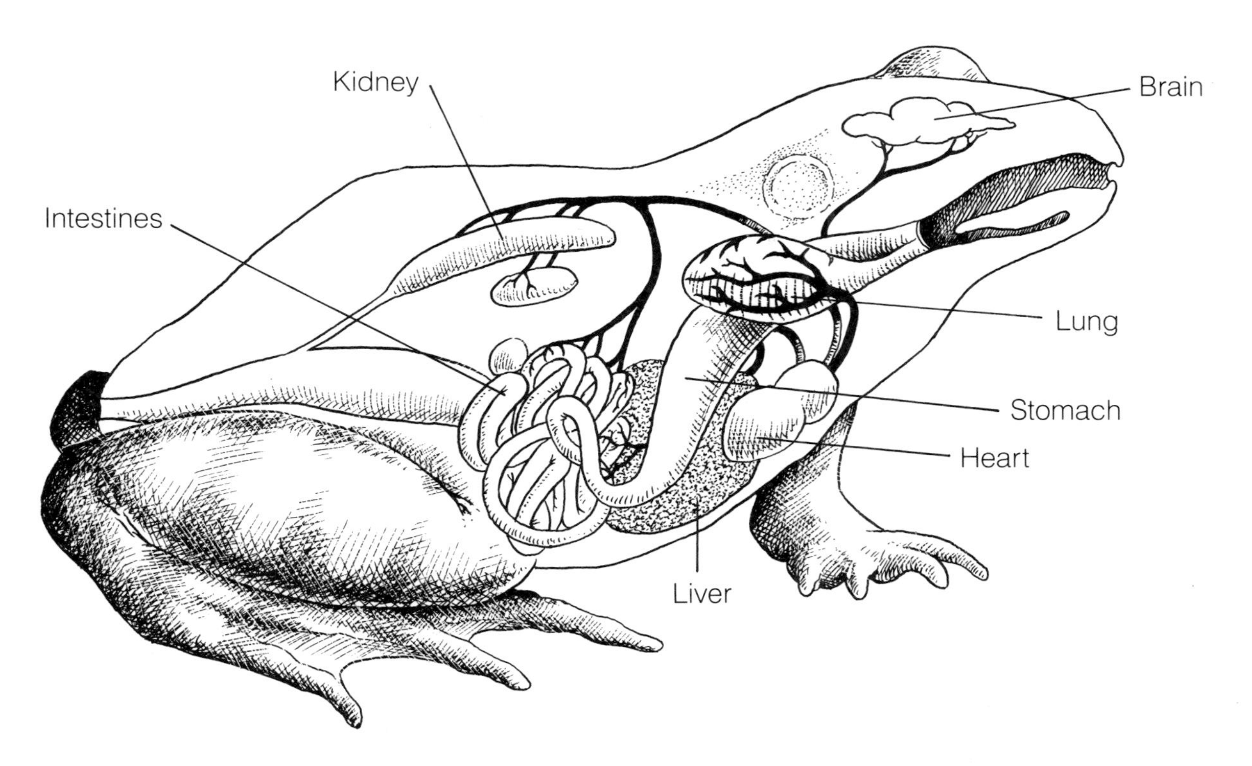

The basic body plan of a frog

by swallowing air and squeezing it down into its lungs. As frogs have almost no ribs and no diaphragm (the muscle between chest and abdomen), they can't breathe with their chests.

Frogs have a larynx or voice-box at the top of their windpipe. This is what they use to croak. Some frogs, such as the *edible frog* of continental Europe, have pouches on the sides of their throat which they can blow out to make their croaking louder. Breathing through the skin is even more important for frogs than breathing through their lungs, which they cannot use when hibernating under water.

The eyes of a frog are well developed and have tear-glands and eyelids that close. It has been discovered that usually their eyes do not pick out anything that is not moving. They are programmed, however, to react to blue and green. When they are threatened, blue means water and safety, while green means grass and spells danger. This means that when they are frightened they will even jump at a piece of blue paper, thinking that it is water. Frogs' eyes bulge and make room when a large object is swallowed, as there is no bone between the roof of the mouth and the eye-socket, just thin sheets of soft tissue.

Frogs hear well and their ears are very sensitive to ground vibrations, which are transmitted through the

Frogs can't 'see' anything that doesn't move

forelegs and shoulders. Amphibians are very sensitive to smells in the air and like snakes have the so-called 'Jacobsen's organ', which enables them to tell what is in the air by flicking out their tongue.

Frogs are very good at jumping. The record is held by the South African *sharp-nosed frog*, which has been known to cover almost 10 m in three leaps. It is said that this frog can jump 4.57 m in a single leap.

In spring, frogs go back to the pond or pool where they were born. The amount of daylight, and the temperature of the moisture in the air tell them when to move, and they may travel up to 3 km to reach their home pond. Frogs are very clever at finding their way: they recognize landmarks, and some species can tell where to go from the position of the sun and stars. In autumn they move from their summer haunts to their hibernation sites, which are often the same pond.

During mating, all the senses of the frog come into play. They are attracted by sounds (mating-calls), smells and sight, as well as touch. Male frogs have highly sensitive 'pimples' on their breasts and toes, and females have similar tiny points on their backs. These are stimulated when they are touched. The skin-colour of a frog can change gradually according to where it lives. This change is controlled by a gland in the brain (the pituitary gland), the same one that tells the frog when it is time to go home to mate.

Each species of frog has its own particular voice, and frogs croak and call for a variety of reasons. Males do so to show off during the mating-season and attract females, or to declare

Some frogs can jump over 4½ m

ownership of territory. Distressed and alarmed frogs often cry out, and the delightful, vividly coloured *tree frogs* of the tropics croak for joy when rain falls!

The frog you are most likely to find in your garden is the *common* or *grass frog*, particularly on damp days or at night. This animal has a yellow to greenish-

Frogs mating on Hampstead Heath

brown skin with numerous blotches and stripes and dark markings. Look at the eyes and see how they are set high on the head – perfect for peeping cautiously out of the water. Notice that the pupils in the eyes run from side to side. The common frog tends to live alone outside the mating-season. The female lays 1000–4000 eggs in a large clump of frogspawn. After the eggs have been deposited in the water they are fertilized by the male, so that they can produce tadpoles.

It is a good thing that female frogs lay so many eggs: most of them never develop into adult frogs. The enemies of the frog are many, and include snakes, mammals such as foxes, otters, hedgehogs and rats, fish such as the pike and perch, and birds such as herons, hawks, seagulls, ducks and geese. Added to this, frogs are attacked by many diseases and parasites (creatures that live on or inside other animals). The frog's greatest enemy, though, is man, who especially over the last 20 years has drained and filled in many ponds and ditches, places where frogs used to live but now cannot. The water in many ponds has been polluted, and the use of insecticides (chemical sprays and the like designed to kill insects) cuts down frogs' food-supply and can cause other damage.

If you want to help the frog, keep your garden pond clean and make sure it is not choked with weeds. Have lots of plants growing round the edge to

Frogs are amphibians not reptiles

provide shade and shelter. Use insecticides as little as possible, and, if you do collect frogspawn in the spring to watch it hatch into tadpoles and see how the tadpoles change into frogs, please make sure that, as soon as the little creatures have grown their hind legs, you release them into the pond or lake where you found the frogspawn.

The Snail

All that most people know about snails is that they move very slowly and that they can be pests in the garden. There is much more than that to them, however. Some are still well under 1 mm long when fully grown, but they are relatives of the octopus, the pearl oyster and the monster giant squid, which grows to a size of 20 m across and battles with sperm whales 5000 m down in the ocean depths. Snails in times gone by were often cruelly treated, particularly in the preparation of folk medicines and charms. Some country people used to think that if they swallowed snails it would stop them coughing!

Snails are members of the group of animals called molluscs, which includes 60,000 species. Molluscs are such

The humble snail is related to the octopus

Snails are molluscs, soft-bodied animals that make mobile homes of shell

successful creatures that they are found nearly everywhere, on land and in water. They have many different designs. Most belong to a sub-group called *Gastropoda*, and, although many have shells protecting their soft bodies, others, such as slugs, do not.

A snail's body consists of a head that can be moved very easily and is packed with sense organs. Behind the head are the internal organs (heart, liver, intestines, and so on) surrounded by a covering of soft tissue. The upper part of this covering is called the 'mantle' and hangs down round the body to enclose a hollow with a damp lining that acts as the lungs and absorbs oxygen for breathing. The lower part of the soft covering is enlarged into a muscular foot which contains a mouth fitted with rows of horny teeth (the 'radula'). This curious design, which allows the snail to gnaw its food with its foot, explains the Latin name *Gastropoda*, which means 'stomach feet'. A snail's blood is not red but colourless and circulates through blood-vessels pumped by a heart with 3 chambers.

The shell is made up of chemicals secreted by the mantle. It is made up of a small amount of a kind of protein mixed with a large amount of chalk. Because the snail needs a source of chalky chemicals, you will not find many snails on acid soils.

The biggest land-snail is the *giant African snail* (which makes a most interesting and cheap pet for a keen young biologist). Its body may be over 20 cm long, and it can weigh as much as 250 gm. The Japanese army brought this snail to the Pacific area during the Second World War as a source of fresh food. At the end of the war the American troops accidentally imported the species into the United States.

A pest: the giant African snail

Because the giant African breeds very quickly and is very destructive, it soon became a problem in farming areas. It has been estimated that one snail can produce around 11 million offspring over a period of 5 years. Attempts have been made to control the vegetarian giant African snail by introducing species of carnivorous snails which prey upon it.

There are 80 species of land-snail in Britain, of which the biggest is the *Roman* or *edible snail*, which occurs in limestone areas in the south and is rather rare. Its body is up to 10 cm long and it weighs up to 90 gm. This snail was introduced by the Romans as food, and has a strong, round, creamy-coloured shell. The *common garden snail* has a round shell that is pale brown with up to 5 dark bands and measures about 35 mm across. Like most snails, it is active mainly at night. During the day it retreats to its favourite damp spot and has a nap. In the winter or if the weather is unusually hot and dry, snails seal up the opening of their shell with a thick sticky film to save the moisture inside.

Snails are 'hermaphrodites', which means that they are not male or female but *both*, so they can *all* lay eggs. However, they still have to mate. During mating, which usually occurs at night in summer, they come together and stab one another with a tiny barbed arrow made of chalk. This injects spermatozoa, living male organisms which then set about fertilizing the female eggs contained within each snail. The eggs, which are tiny and white, are laid in batches of up to 40 in holes in the soil. After 4 weeks or so, perfect mini-snails emerge.

Other land-snails which you may come across in the garden include the *moss snail*, which has a light brown body and a long cone-shaped shell around 6 mm long that is shiny and pale to dark-brown in colour. This snail loves damp moss, piles of dead leaves and compost-heaps. The *tree snail* has a long, cone-shaped, brownish or greenish shell about 10 mm long, and may be seen on tree-trunks or dry stone walls in gardens. The *white-lipped banded snail* has a shiny, thin, round shell about 17 mm wide and 20 mm high, slightly flattened on the sides. The shell-colour varies, but is often yellow, with up to 5 dark bands. The snail's body is greenish-grey. The *dark-lipped banded snail* has a much thicker and more rounded shell about 22 mm wide and 25 mm high; the colour varies from yellow to brown and the number of bands varies too. The body is greyish-yellow. The colours and markings of banded snails' shells depend on where the snails live, helping them blend into their surroundings more easily. They are darker in woodland than in gardens because woodland colours are darker than garden colours. My favourite garden snail is the tiny (5 mm high and wide) *garlic glass snail*, which emits a strong smell of garlic if upset or handled.

One of the snail's great enemies, the thrush

Snails can live for up to 10 years, but they have lots of enemies. The most famous is the thrush, which uses a stone to crack open their shells and eat their soft bodies.

A snail 'family snapshot'

Discover the animals which
live in your house

The Mouse

Mice are not ferocious animals, though a wild one will give a sharp bite if you pick it up, but they are important pests. They carry diseases and harm food-supplies, not only by eating them but also by damaging and soiling what they don't eat. Mice even helped to lose a war!

In 1796 the Austrians were facing defeat by Napoleon's armies. The Austrian generals did not know what to do, so they decided to use an ancient Greek and Roman way of working out a plan. They dipped a mouse's feet in some ink and placed the animal on a map of the battlefield. It ran across the map leaving a splodgy path, and the generals sent their soldiers to the places marked by the mouse. It didn't help though, for Napoleon won.

Mice were bred, protected and worshipped in ancient Greece and Rome. As you can tell from the story about the Austrian generals who copied the old practice of using a mouse to tell them what to do, they were thought to be magical creatures. Mouse-worship continued in Greece right up to the sixteenth century.

There are old country people alive who as children were given roasted, stewed or baked mice to eat, and some people still believe that mouse is a good cure for coughs, sore throats, fevers, fits, whooping-cough and even bed-wetting! I've tasted cooked mouse, and it reminded me of tender chicken. In earlier times, mouse blood was believed to get rid of warts on the skin if dropped on them, and a seventeenth-century treatment for quinsy (a disease like tonsilitis) was to swallow a silk thread

The mouse that lost a war

The house mouse, a typical rodent

dipped in mouse-blood. There were many other such 'cures'.

There are some very strange legends about mice. One is that in the year 970 AD an army of mice ate alive a German bishop called Hatto in a tower on the river Rhine. The name of the tower is the Mausturm, German for 'Mouse Tower'. However, it hasn't really got anything to do with mice, and its name comes from an old German word like the word for mouse but really meaning 'toll'. Boats passing up and down the river had to pay a toll, a sort of tax, before they would be allowed to continue on their way. People must have forgotten what the name really meant, and thought up a story to explain what the tower had to do with mice. Of course mice would never eat a bishop! The typical mouse is a much shyer and more timid animal, which is what the Scottish poet Robert Burns meant when he called it a 'cow'ring, tim'rous beastie' in his famous poem about a mouse.

Like rats, mice are rodents, mammals with *one* pair of upper gnawing teeth. The difference between rats and mice is not just one of size, for there are small species of rat and large species of mouse. To scientists rats and mice are simply names given to various species within the animal family *Muridae*. Rats have more rows of scales on their tails than mice have. Rats have 210 or more, while mice never have more than 180.

You have probably seen the dull-coloured little *house mouse* and, of course, the pretty little mice bred as pets. These tame mice are very clean, and cheap to keep. But there are many other sorts of mouse in the world today. The *birch mice* of the Russian steppes leap rather than run, live in burrows and hibernate during the bitter winters. The *grasshopper mice* of North America share burrows with prairie dogs and are useful in controlling insects, their favourite food, and sometimes kill birds or other rodents. *Jumping mice* can be found in America, and there are some little-known varieties in the forests of China where the giant panda lives. They have grey, golden or yellow-brown fur, long hind legs and very long tails. Jumping mice have a wonderful sense of balance, owing to their enlarged middle ear. They also have very sharp hearing. America live over 60 species of *deer mice*, pretty creatures with big eyes. They come in lots of different colours, from white to brown and black, but always have white feet. In Australia, sure enough, there is a mouse with a pouch, the *marsupial mouse*. Despite its name, however, it is not really a mouse at all, but a tiny cousin of the kangaroo. Just like other marsupials, it carries its babies in its pouch.

Mice can spread disease to humans

The *spiny pocket mice* of the Mexican deserts have very rough fur. Russia has the delicate *Selevin's mouse*, which nobody knew about until it was discovered in 1939. This interesting little creature loves to feed on spiders and is very active at night. It can't stand more than a few minutes of sunshine without becoming ill! Between Alaska, in the far north of the American continent, and the southern tip of South

These are just a few of the many types of mice in the world. They are tough little creatures, spread very quickly and have adapted to all sorts of surroundings. House mice have been known to live within the walls of refrigerators, and to keep themselves warm in their chilly surroundings have grown longer fur!

In the wild, mice tend not to live very long – only a few weeks or months. Pet mice usually live much longer, and can reach ages of $3\frac{1}{2}$ and sometimes even $5\frac{1}{2}$ years. Mice have an in-built ability to find their way home, but they are almost certainly colour-blind and see everything in black and white.

Like most small rodents, including rats, they need to drink very little water and usually produce nearly all they need from the food they eat. Desert species such as the *spiny mouse* can survive happily without drinking at all. To store the water in their bodies as long as possible, such species produce few droppings and only a little urine, which is very thick. Some spiny mice can live solely on tiny amounts of sea-water, and even your ordinary house mouse can go for ages without drinking anything. Do remember, though, to make sure that your pet mice always have a supply of clean, fresh water, as they are less hardy than their wild cousins and need to be able to have a drink when they want it.

Wild mice eat all sorts of things. They will eat scraps of rotten food and even rabbit droppings! Mice that live out in the country live mainly on fruit, seeds and insects, and all mice like these if they can get them. Of course, the food they are most famous for liking is cheese, but really it is not one of their favourites at all. If you give too much of it to your pet mouse, it will make its urine very smelly. It just is not true

Shall I or shan't I?

what R.R. Kirk says in his poem 'The Mice':

> The mice were not impressed by that
>   great house
> Wherein you have your glory and
>   your ease;
> Magnificence is wasted on a mouse;
> They judge all things by cheese.

The tail of the mouse is used for balancing and for holding on to things. Because it is not covered with fur, it also provides a way of getting rid of heat when the mouse is too hot. Mice in colder places need and have shorter tails than mice in warmer areas. This is why the tails of mice that live in southern Britain are 10–15 per cent shorter than the tails of mice living in the far north of the country.

Some tame mice 'dance' or 'waltz'.

A safe descent from cheese mountain

Like the white and coloured varieties you can buy in pet shops, these mice have been specially bred from types of house mice. They have something wrong with their inner ears and this affects their sense of balance, so that they reel about and seem to dance.

It has even been found that mice have some ability to survive under water. A scientist has kept mice for up to 18 hours in tanks of salt water filled with oxygen under high pressure. The mice 'breathed' the water and their lungs picked up the oxygen from the water, as well as they usually do from air. However, under normal conditions, where the water would contain much less oxygen, it is unlikely that the mice would have lasted so long without drowning. They are, after all, land mammals, and not designed to live under water. Do *not* try this experiment for yourself!

Everyone knows that the mouse can move very fast, and lots of other things about it seem to be speeded up. The heart of a mouse beats at the incredibly rapid rate of 500–700 beats a minute. The animal also breathes very quickly – about 80–230 times a minute. The female mouse can carry her babies inside her for as little as 13 days before they are born, though usually the gestation period (the time it takes for a baby to grow inside its mother) lasts for 19–21 days. This is one of the shortest gestation periods among mammals, whose babies are born fully developed, looking like small adults. There are 1–20 young mice in each litter (group of babies), and the mother has several litters each year. Mother mice feed their babies for about 3 weeks, and a mouse is fully grown when it is 6–8 weeks old.

House mice are not welcome in the house and people use cats, traps and poisons to get rid of them. But we should not forget that dormice, relatives of the house mouse who live in the countryside, are in danger because so many of the places where they live are being destroyed and because of the new methods used in farming. These delightful, harmless creatures badly need our help and support. Just because one species of mouse is a pest, we must not think that all species of mouse are as bad.

The basic body-plan of the mouse

The Woodlouse

You will often find the woodlouse about the house – in the cellar, in a pile of old timber, in the greenhouse or in the garden shed. In its armour plating the woodlouse looks like a tiny armadillo or a miniature tank. Most people know nothing about this little creature, which likes to mess about around wood.

The group of Crustaceans to which the woodlouse belongs are called *Isopods*. The Isopods are a varied group and highly successful species most of which live in water (salt water or fresh). Indeed, the woodlouse is the only Isopod that lives on land and breathes air. The other Isopods all look fairly similar to woodlice. Some are giants 35 cm long and 12 cm broad and live deep in the ocean. Some have been found at depths of almost 10,000 m, and others 4000 m above sea-level in the South America Andes. Some swim free in the sea; others burrow in the mud of beaches and swamps. One widespread species,

The woodlouse: not an insect

The woodlouse is not an insect, or a relative of the armadillo (which is a mammal), but a relative of the lobster, the crab, the shrimp and the prawn. Like them, it is a member of a large family of animals with bodies that are composed of 19 segments and covered by hard outer 'crusts' (exo-skeletons). They are called *Crustaceans*.

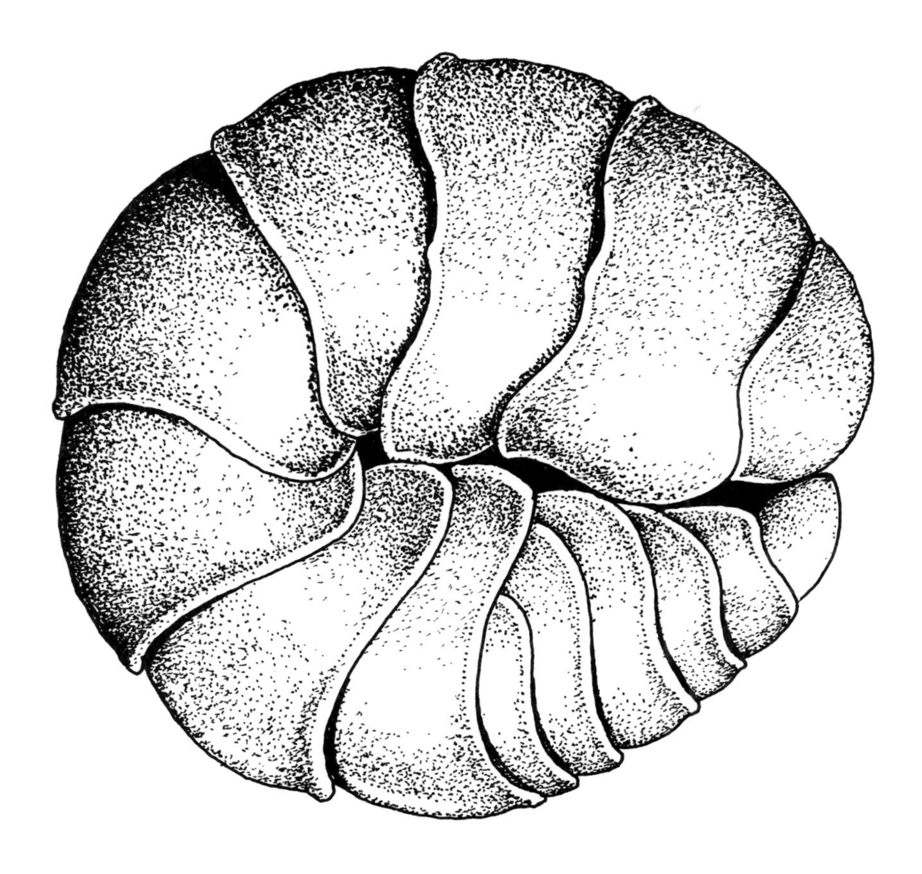

called the *gribble*, is only 3 mm long but it does a lot of damage by boring into timber under water (for instance, the wooden jetties where boats tie up, and the pilings that hold up seaside piers). Up to 70 gribbles per square centimetre have been found on badly infested timber.

Our friend the woodlouse, however, does not cause any trouble. It's a shy and nervous creature and one common British species that is found especially in areas with chalk soil has a tendency to roll up into a ball when alarmed. This is why it is called the *pill bug*.

Some years ago I tasted a favourite food of people who live in some parts of Africa – salted woodlice. They are eaten rather as we eat salted peanuts, as a handy snack. Don't turn your nose up at this! What's so odd about it when we eat the shrimps, the prawn and the crab, relatives of the woodlouse?

Hard 'crust' and 'roll up' give defence

Around 50 species of woodlouse make their homes in Britain. All have the usual armoured body-casing, but, as this is not very waterproof, they must keep out of the sun and live in damp, shady places. Otherwise most of them would dry up and die. The pill bug, however, can survive better in dry places, and you will quite often find it in warm parts of the house. Woodlice come out of their hidy-holes at night, when there is no sun to trouble them and most birds are asleep. They feed on bits of decaying plant, on soft green leaves and on moulds and other fungi. They find their food by using their antennae, which are sensitive to smell. Their insides give board and lodging to lots of friendly bacteria, which pass out with their droppings. Woodlouse-droppings look like tiny balls or pellets and you may be

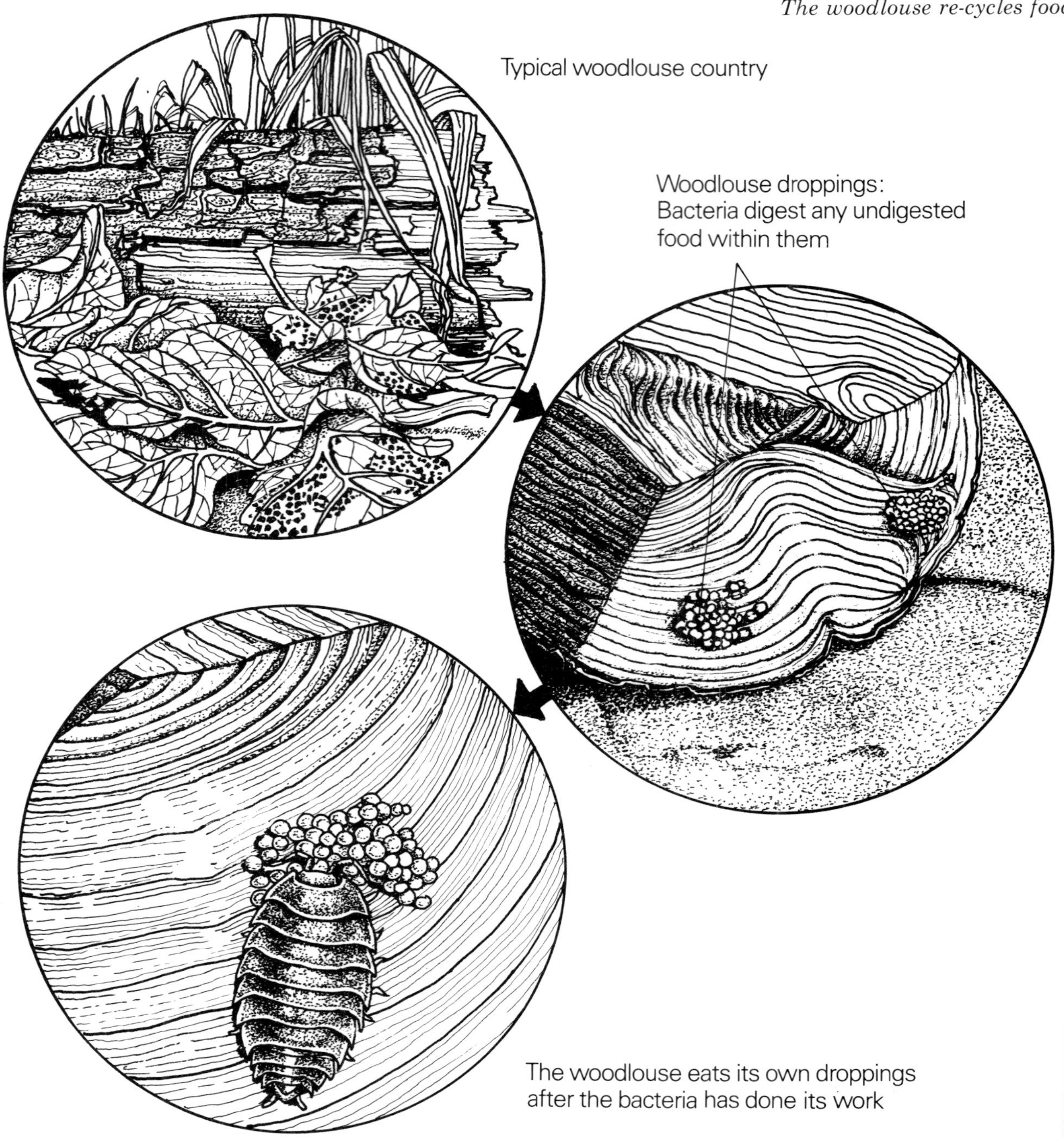

able to find some under a log or stone. The bacteria digest any undigested food in the droppings and then the woodlouse eats the droppings, so that it can use the food the bacteria have digested for it. (Food that has been digested is food the body can use.) You may see your pet rabbit eating its own droppings. It does it for the same reason as the woodlouse does. This process for using food again is called 'recycling', and it is good for the soil.

The commonest species of woodlouse is (surprise, surprise!) the *common woodlouse*, which is up to 15 mm long and has a medium- to dark-grey body with pale edges to the 'armour'. Like insects and other animals that carry their skeletons on the outside of their bodies, the woodlouse has to shed its outer shell in order to be able to grow. It moults in two parts: it sheds the front half of its shell one day, and the back half perhaps up to a week later. You may be lucky enough to find a half-new, half-old woodlouse part-way through moulting.

The female woodlouse deposits her eggs into pouches of liquid on the underside of her body. After 3–5 weeks, the eggs hatch – not as grubs, but as perfect tiny woodlice. The youngsters take about 2 years to mature and may live for a further 1–2 years.

Woodlice are fascinating and harmless creatures, and in the garden or greenhouse they do a useful job by recycling plant material. So be kind to the woodlouse when you next see it in the cellar or attic – it's one of the humblest and most ancient members of the house zoo.

Common woodlice

A family party in the potting shed

The Spider

There's an old saying that goes, 'If you wish to live and thrive, let the spider run alive.' Spiders are supposed to bring good luck, and in Britain and other cooler countries are useful and harmless to man.

Spiders have been thought lucky for hundreds of years, and there is an ancient legend which says that a spider protected the infant Jesus and his parents during their flight into Egypt. Pursued by Herod's soldiers, they hid in a cave and a spider at once wove a thick web across the cave-mouth. A dove alighted on the web and laid an egg among the strands, and when the soldiers arrived at the cave and saw the web and the egg lying there, they assumed that no one could possibly have entered the cave for a long time and went on their way without looking inside.

Spiders are not insects but members of a group of animals called *Arachnids*. Like insects, these animals are arthropods (creatures that have joints in their legs), but they have no wings and have 8 legs (insects have 6). Other

The legend of Jesus and the spider

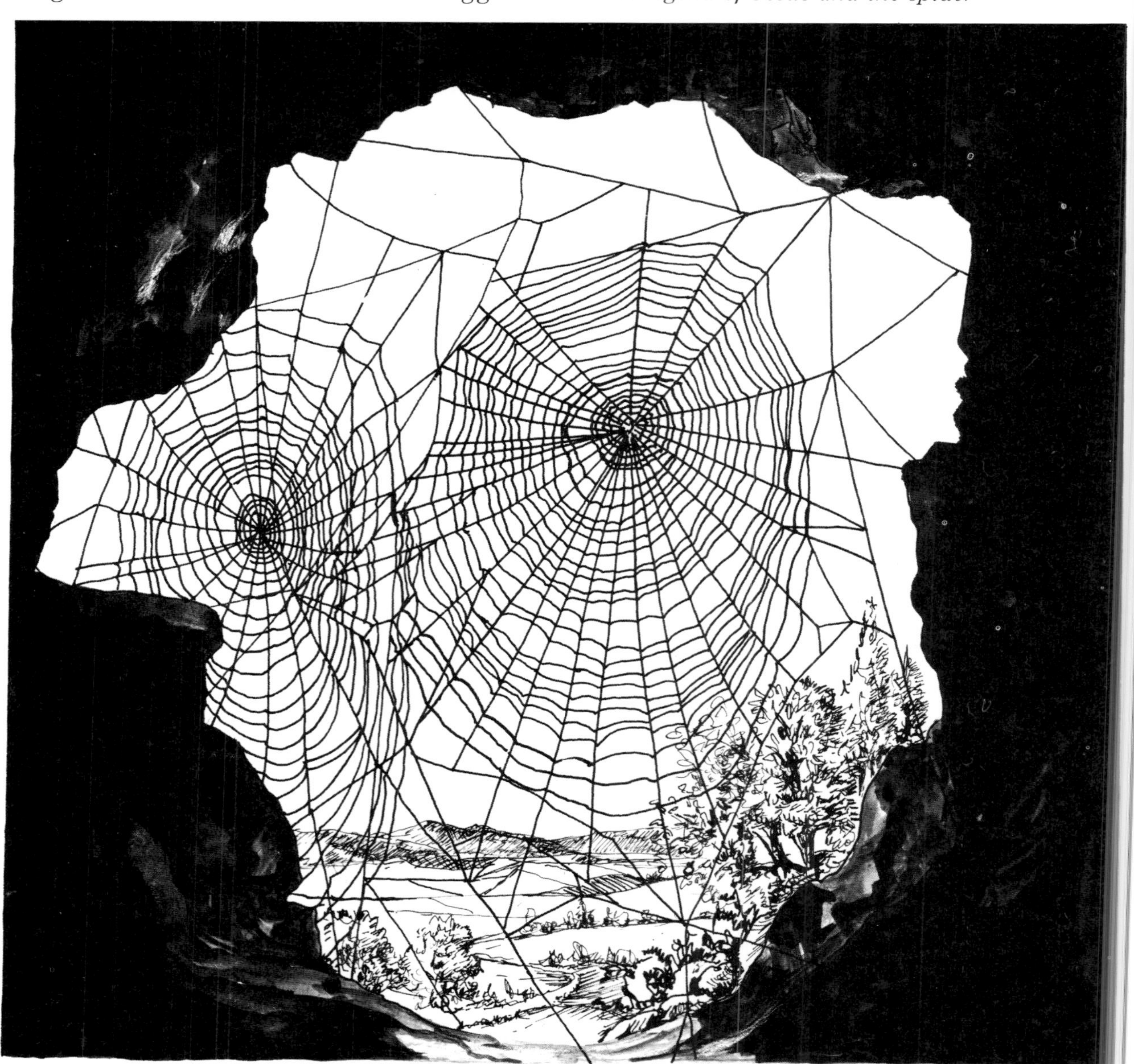

The spider wove a web to hide the cavemouth

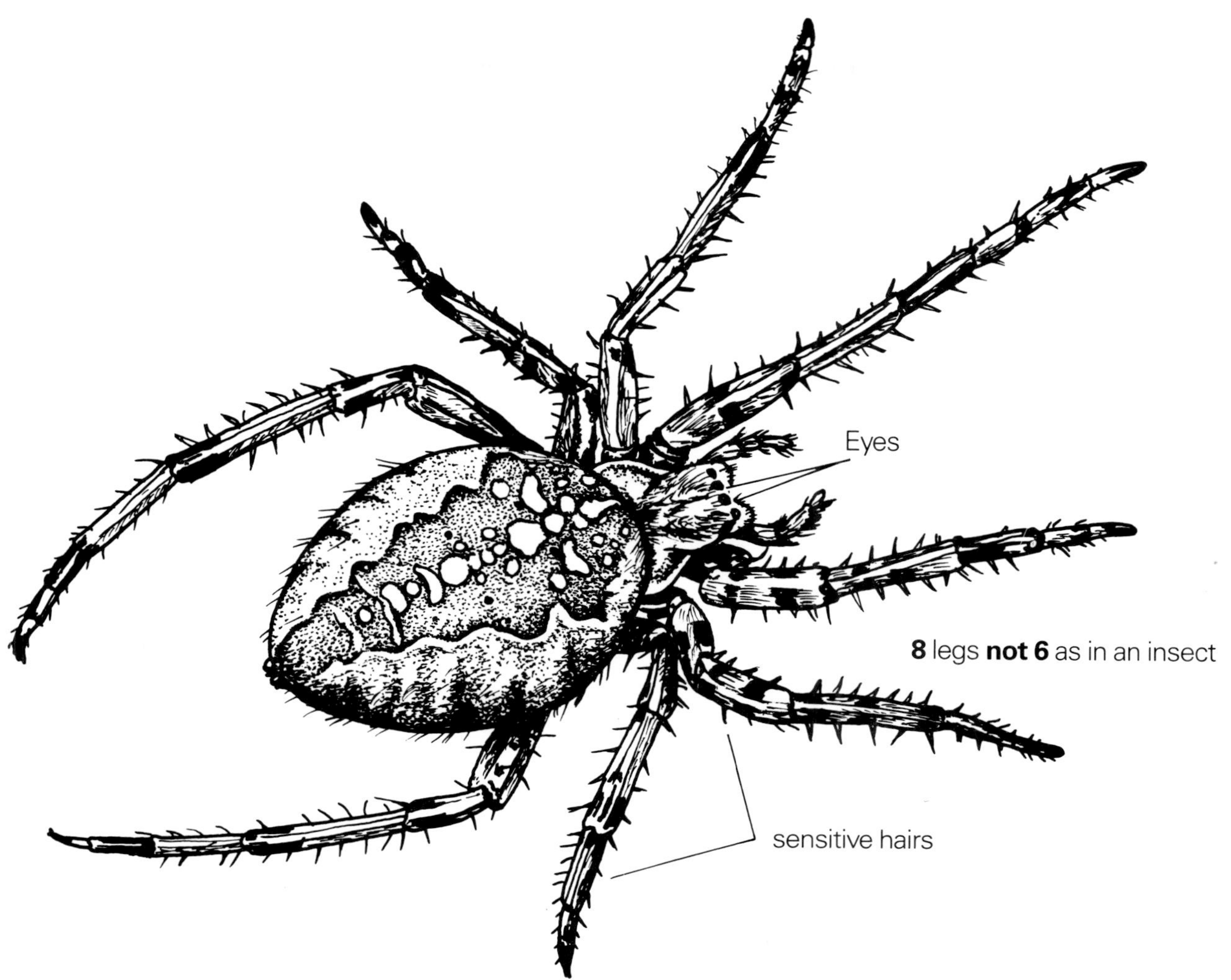

Body plan of typical spider

Arachnids are scorpions, ticks and mites. They breathe through a network of air-filled tubes in the body-surface and in some cases through organs called 'book lungs', which are similar to a fish's gills. Like other arthropods, such as insects and Crustaceans, Arachnids have a hard body shell or 'exo-skeleton' that has to be shed from time to time so that the creature can grow. Arachnids have no antennae, but the sensitive hairs or bristles on their body and legs act in a similar way to antennae.

The earliest known spider lived 370 million years ago. There are now approximately 40,000 species in the world, from Greenland and Alaska in the north to the southern tip of South America. Some live under water and

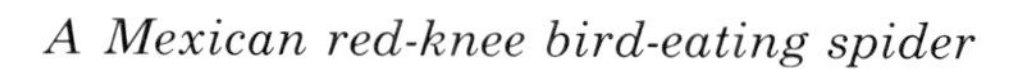

A Mexican red-knee bird-eating spider

others at up to 7300 m above sea-level. The biggest spider in the world is the famous *bird-eating spider*, which can be 25 cm across with its legs stretched out. Although it might not look it, it is not at all dangerous to man; but it still needs to be handled carefully. It can sometimes give a painful bite and the hairs on its body may cause an itchy rash on the skin.

British spiders range in size from the *six-eyed spider*, which has a body about 2 cm long, to a rare kind of *money spider* found so far only in a New Forest swamp and on a heath in Surrey. Its body is only 1 mm long. Abroad there are even smaller spiders; one kind that lives in moss in the Pacific island of Samoa is less than 0.5 mm long.

Not all spiders spin webs, but most of those you will find around the house do. The *house spider*'s web is usually quite closely meshed (with the strands quite close together) and can be 15 cm across (compare that to the webs of Australian and Indian spiders, which may be 3 m or even 5 m wide! The *daddy-long-legs spider*, which is commoner in the south of England than further north, spins a fine, very flimsy web. The *four-spotted orb spider* is red-brown in colour with four white spots, and is usually seen in the garden, and the yellow and black *spitting spider* squirts a jet of silk at its prey from a distance of up to 10 mm, binding it to a wall or a plant stem.

British spiders that do not make webs include the large *wolf spider*, which has a long black body with an orange-yellow stripe down the middle of its back. When resting, it holds its two pairs of front legs close together. I often see this spider hunting around the pool in my back garden. The *buzzing spider* is very common in gardens and has a pale-coloured body with dark, arrow-like markings. The *zebra spider* is striped black and white, can jump up to 10 cm and is fond of walls and windows, while the *common crab spider* has a plump white or yellow body and is to be found in gardens in southern England.

The harmless house spider

The *house spider* is the species most often found in the house zoo. It is dull brown and up to 10 mm long. Often this spider turns up in the bath or sink – not because it's climbed up the drain, but because it's fallen in or come for a drink of water (there's usually a little near the plug-hole). As the sides of the bath or sink are smooth, the spider can't climb up again, because it doesn't have the sticky feet of insects such as the cockroach.

The spitting spider, a spitter

The zebra spider, a jumper

A crab spider eats a robber fly

Like all spiders, house spiders are marvellously made. They have glands that feed poison to their fangs, and after killing their prey they suck in its body-juices. House spiders and all other British spiders cannot injure humans; indeed, all the spiders that catch their prey in webs tend not to use their poison at all, except when it is the only way to defend themselves.

Spiders possess a highly developed nervous-system. The house spider can see fairly well, and the wolf spider uses the sun as a compass in a similar way to bees, but the most important of all the senses to a spider is the sense of touch. Web-building spiders send messages by 'plucking' at the strands of their webs. Males signal to females. Warning or feeding signals are sent by a mother to her young. Some male spiders attach a thread to the female's web and then use it as a sort of 'phone line, by plucking it with a certain rhythm. A spider can immediately tell what sort of creature has been caught in its web – a bee, a fly or some other insect – by the vibrations it feels. If the prey is a large and dangerous animal such as a bee, the spider may decide simply to cut it free. Spiders have a poor sense of smell, but scientists think that they can hear well.

Most fascinating is a spider's silk-making ability. On the abdomen are 'spinnerets', which are used to form silk

Nature's brilliant designer

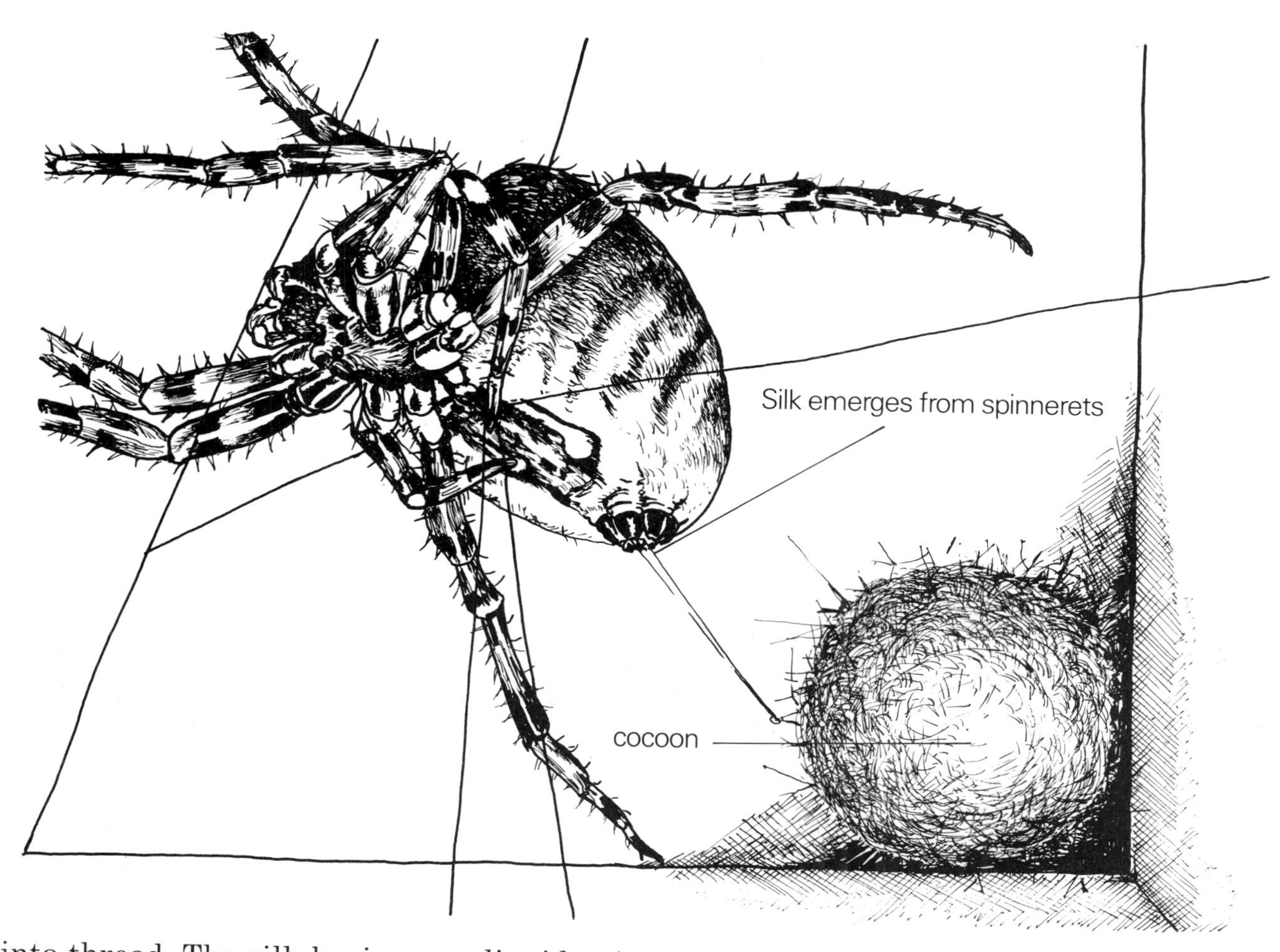

Spider silk is used in cocoons

into thread. The silk begins as a liquid made by special glands in the body, passes through the spinnerets and comes out at the tips of special hollow hairs called spinning-tubes on the end of the spinnerets. As soon as it comes out into the air the liquid silk turns into thread. Each silken thread produced by the spider is in fact a rope composed of many fine single threads each only about 0.0003 mm across. Spider silk is finer, lighter and stronger than silk-worm silk, but, unlike silkworm farms, spider-silk farms have never made much money. Most species of spider use their silk for purposes other than catching insects: they use it to make cocoons for eggs, to line their burrows, to make hinges for trap-doors, and so on. Some spiders can use up to 4000 m of thread to make just one cocoon. By coating their feet with a special oil, spiders make sure they do not get caught in their own web.

Female spiders lay eggs in silken cocoons. The baby spiders or 'spiderlings' hatch from the eggs, and live on egg yolk stored in their intestines until the yolk is all used up and their digestive systems are ready for more solid food. When this happens, they go off on their own before getting hungry and starting to eat one another! As they grow they moult about 7 or 8 times, shedding the entire skin and also the cornea (the clear front part of the eye), the lining of part of the digestive system and the breathing organs. House spiders are the second longest-living British species, sometimes living for 7 years.

Never forget that spiders are useful members of the house zoo.

The Bat

As evening falls, day begins for the animal that is the most endangered of all the characters in the house zoo – the bat or 'flittermouse'. How lucky you are if your roof or a nearby church-tower has been chosen as home by this creature, the only mammal that can really fly.

In the past, people thought of the bat as an evil creature that drinks blood. It was linked with bad luck, death and witchcraft. Some people still think like this, but it's all a lot of nonsense – or nearly all, for there is one South American bat that feeds on blood. All the other bats are wonderful, harmless animals who are man's friends. Despite this, it is because of man that the number of bats in Britain and in many other countries is falling. New houses do not have places for bats to live in. The treatment of old timbers with chemicals (for woodworm and other pests) can kill bats by poisoning them. There are also fewer good hunting-grounds for bats to catch insects. All the British species of bat have suffered, but at least they are now strictly

Long-eared bat and moth

protected by the law.

It is good to see old superstitions about bats dying away. The idea that bats can get tangled up in your hair is rubbish – the bat's sonar beam, which helps it to find a moth in total darkness and tells it when there is any obstacle in the way so that it can avoid bumping into it, means that it is hardly likely even to brush against a human head! The sonar beam is a stream of high-pitched sounds that the bat sends out. These bounce off anything in the bat's flight-path, and return as echoes to the bat's ears so that it can tell where it is. Man has learned from the bat and developed a system called radar, like the bat's sonar, that aeroplanes use so that they can fly by night.

A quarter of all species of mammal are bats: there are 951 different kinds of bat in the world today. The names of some of the species are quite delightful. Among them are *dawn bats*, *leaf-nosed bats*, *bulldog bats*, *thumbless bats*, *wrinkle-lipped bats*, *fish-eating bats*, *red bats*, *grey bats*, *brown bats*, *bamboo bats* and *painted bats*. I think my favourite is the *butterfly bat*, which has white spots and stripes in its fur and patterned wings. When it hangs in a tree, it looks just like a twist of dead leaves.

My favourite, the butterfly bat

Bats feed on lots of different things, and each species tends to have one favourite food. This can be insects, scorpions, shrimps, mice, other bats, lizards, frogs, fish, fruit, flowers, pollen and even the blood of other animals. The species found in Britain eat insects, and the *horseshoe bat* loves to hunt cockchafers in the spring.

Some bats can migrate over distances as great as 2000 km. Their wings flap, so that unlike other mammals they really do fly. Creatures such as flying squirrels do not really fly at all: they simply

stretch out flaps of skin along the side of the body so that they can glide down from trees. The bat often uses its wings to catch insects, with the bit between the hind legs acting as a sort of scoop. Some bats can fly at almost 40 miles per hour.

Certain species of bat, such as *flying foxes*, can see very well, and *fruit-eating bats* have a good sense of smell. Most species rely on an incredibly highly developed sense of hearing, which allows them to fly and hunt in the dark by using their sonar beam. The ears are big, and bats' faces, which many people think are ugly, are specially designed to pick up sound. The bat's sonar bleeps, which are usually too high for humans to hear, are made through the mouth or, in some species, the nose. Some bats can continue sending out sounds while feeding, by 'whistling' through a gap in their teeth.

While some species migrate to warmer places in winter, many others hibernate

Bat faces are hardly pretty

The bat's amazing sonar system

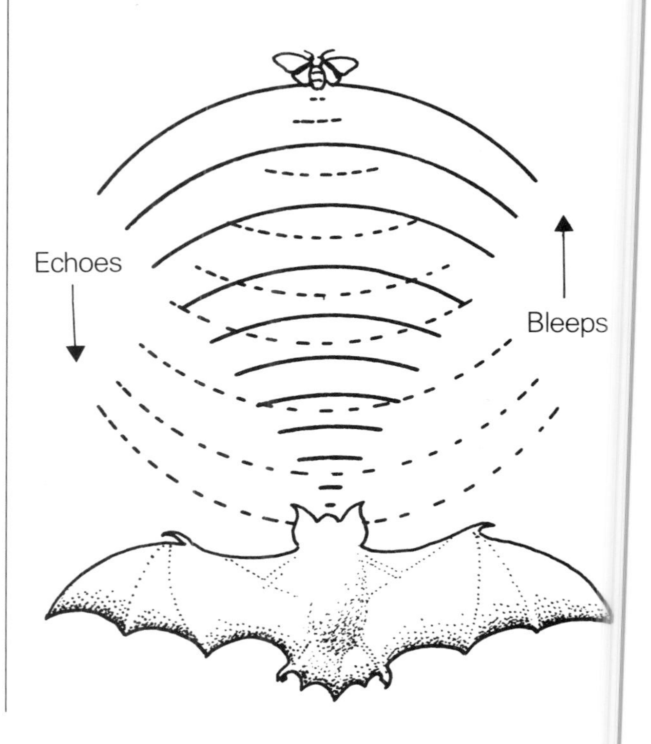

during cold weather. They select suitable hide-outs, such as caves or treeholes, where it is warm and damp. This helps them to do without water while they are asleep. When they have found the right place, they become dozy, their body temperature drops, and their breathing-rate and heart-beat slow down. This saves energy and stops the body fat from being used up too quickly. During summer and autumn, bats get ready for hibernation by building up their body fat. When they wake in spring, they may have lost one third of their body weight. During hibernation they wake up from time to time – in order to urinate! Bats can reach an age of 30 years or more.

One bat, the *vampire bat* from South America, lives by drinking the blood of domestic animals and sometimes that of human beings. Vampire bats are very fussy about which victims they attack. They prefer certain breeds of cattle and also select cows rather than bulls and calves rather than adults. The vampire bat can carry many diseases, including the terrible rabies.

The only dangerous bat: the vampire

The Fungus

Zoos need other living things besides animals. Animals need plants for food and shelter, and plants often need animals to pollinate them and destroy pests. The good zoo not only uses plants as a food source for vegetarian species, but also makes important use of trees, bushes, grass and flowers to help the animals feel at home. Humans in the zoo in the house like to have plants around them, and there must be few homes without a garden, window-box, potted plants or vases of flowers. But other plants come uninvited to make their home in the house zoo. Of these the commonest by far are the fungi, which I think the most bizarre and interesting members of the plant kingdom.

A bad case of dry rot

Fungi are a vast group of plants which do not possess the green chemical chlorophyll, which other plants use to make food from carbon dioxide, a gas in the air. Some fungi are the lowest known forms of plant life. They have bodies which are either simple cells or branching tubes. They reproduce by means of spores or 'seed' cells. As they cannot make their own food they have to pinch it either from dead plants or animals (fungi that do this are called 'saprophytes') or, less commonly, from living things (as 'parasites'). Some fungi can obtain food in either way. Most fungi are saprophytes and they are a most important part of the never-ending cycle of death and life in nature. All sorts of waste material and dead and decaying things are food for fungi: old leaves, the remains of plants, broken branches and fallen trees, and the droppings and dead bodies of animals.

Most fungi, of which there are at least 120,000 species, live in parts of the world where it is fairly warm and damp. They are everywhere, and are one of the oldest kind of living things, although their soft and delicate tissues do not show up well in fossils.

The most familiar fungus is the edible mushroom and there are many other varieties of 'toadstool' to be found in the woods and fields, particularly in autumn, ranging from the pretty but poisonous *fly agaric* to the *black* or *white truffle*, which lives underground in beech-woods and is considered a great delicacy. Some fungi are very useful indeed to man; the yeasts that make bread rise and are used to make hops into beer and grape-juice into wine are all fungi, and so are the moulds from which penicillin and other antibiotics (used to fight all sorts of illnesses) are made. Other fungi cause disease in humans and other creatures.

But about the house the fungi you're most likely to come across are the moulds. These white, green or black furry patches can be found growing on stale food of every kind, on jam, damp clothing and leather, wallpaper and plaster. If you have a microscope, scrape some mould off an old crust of bread and magnify it as much as you can.

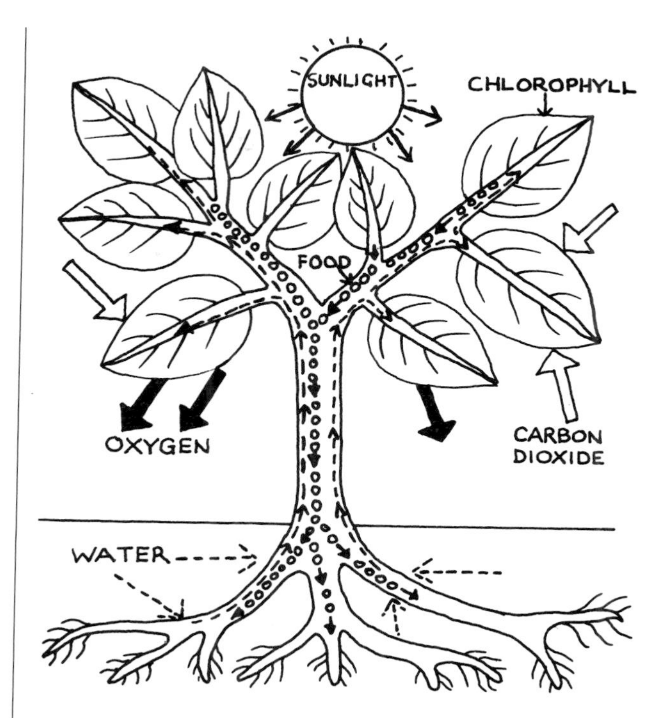

Unlike plants, the fungus does not make food

You'll easily see the network of hyphae (small branching tubes) and the darker, rounded spore-containing bodies. Where do the moulds come from? As I have said, these fungi are everywhere, and

A mouldy piece of bread

their spores, too tiny to see without a microscope, blow about in the wind and draughts and are dropped all over the place. When the spores land on something they can grow on, they absorb water and swell. The outer coat breaks open and a tube sprouts. This

Hyphae and spores of a fungus

tube soon begins to branch and is the beginning of a new network of hyphae. The hyphae absorb liquids from the food the fungus is growing on, and help the process by passing out enzymes, which break down the food so that it can be absorbed easily.

Other very unwelcome fungi in the house zoo are the species that cause 'dry rot'. These fungi feed on timber, making it lighter, weaker and more brittle. Eventually the wood warps and cracks if the dry rot is not treated. Here again we see a fungus living on dead plant material. The hyphae of the dry-rot fungus work their way into wood, absorbing food, while on the surface the fungus may form thick layers shaped like cakes (or even mushrooms). Although the disease is called '*dry* rot', the fungi that cause it need water to be able to live, although they cannot attack wood that is too wet. 'Wet rot', on the other hand, is caused by fungi that like lots of water. Some dry-rot

The effect of wet-rot fungus

Lichens: signs of pure air

fungi can carry water with them over long distances, and can cause dry rot in wood that would otherwise be too dry to be affected.

Other fungi are harmless, pretty and welcome members of the house zoo. If you live in a stone house, you may be lucky enough to find lichens growing on the walls outside. Lichens are a mixture of two sorts of plant – fungus and algae (tiny blue-green plants that contain the chemical chlorophyll). The fungus provides water and salts, and the spores that allow the lichen to spread, and the algae feed the fungus with sugary food. The two need each other to survive, and the process whereby they work together is called 'symbiosis'.

Lichens demand clean air and will not grow where there is chemical pollution. They grow very, very slowly, with some species making no progress at all for up to 50 years. Even the fastest-spreading lichens don't grow more than 1 cm per year. A good place to find lichens is on the gravestones of country churchyards.

Close-up of lichens

The Silverfish

You must have seen this little creature. It's often found under the paper that lines cupboard drawers or larder shelves, beneath draining-boards and in other damp spots, and in garden sheds. The silverfish is about 15 mm long, and has a gleaming, silvery, narrow body with three little 'prongs' sticking out from the tail end. Because the silverfish likes sweet, sugary or starchy foods, it seeks flour and sugar in kitchens, breadcrumbs in larders, and glue in cardboard boxes.

The silverfish has been around for over 30 million years and is one of the most primitive types of insect still alive. It is a true insect, with a segmented body, 6 legs and 2 antennae, but it has no wings and it does not seem that the ancestors of silverfish ever had them. The first insects evolved from worm-like animals that were beginning to grow legs. A remarkable creature called the *Peripatus* shows us how the change probably happened and has some of the features of the worm and some of the features of the arthropods – animals, such as insects, with joints in their legs so that they can bend them. After this early stage, it seems, most insects began to grow wings, but not all of them did. Silverfish are such insects – reminders of an ancient time in the evolution of insects.

A silverfish, not a fish

The 'silverfish' is so called because of

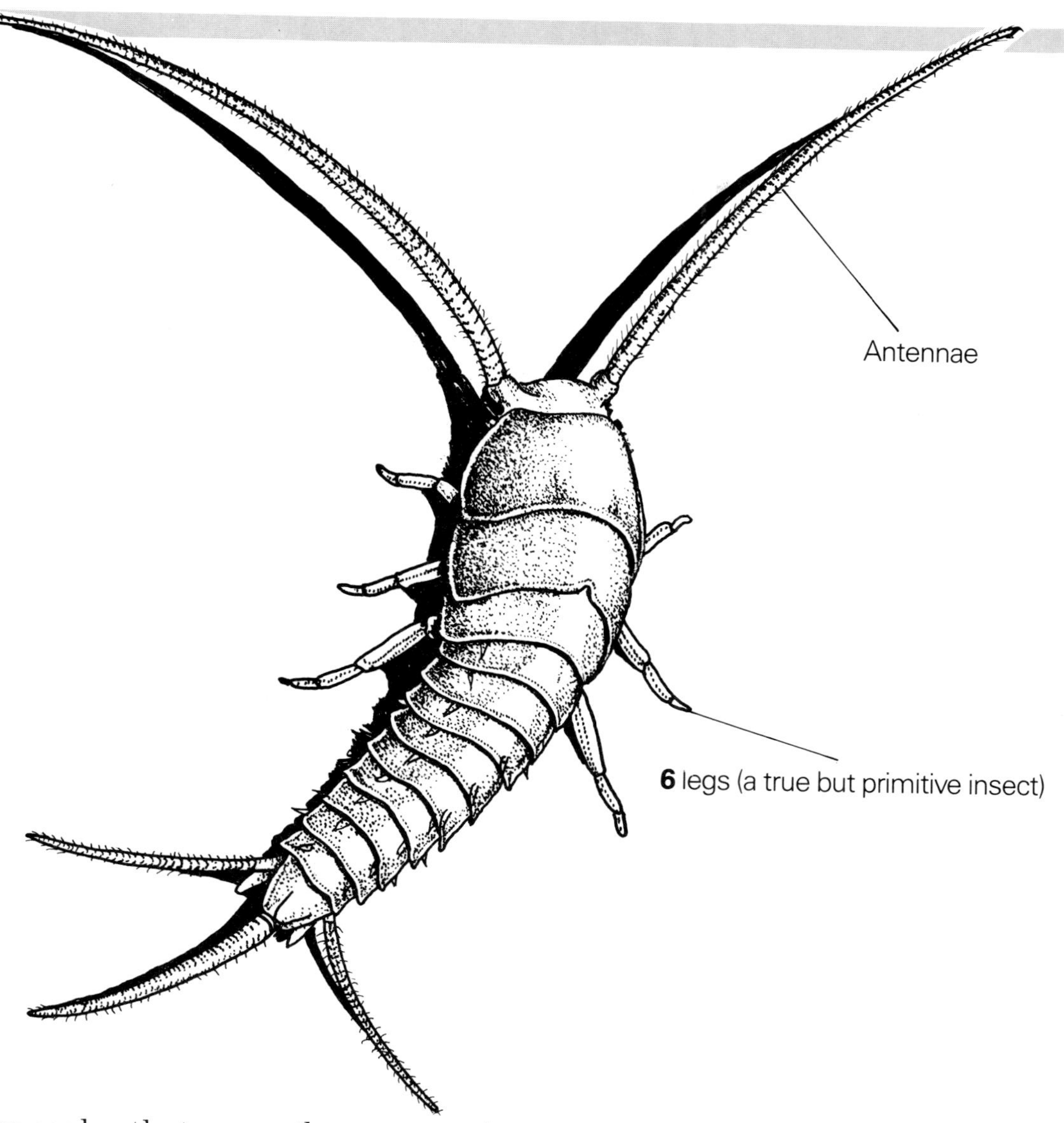

The body plan of the silverfish

the silvery scales that cover the abdomen, and the 'prongs' at the tail end, which look something like a fish's tail. Silverfish do not like dry rooms or light. They will eat almost any form of animal or vegetable matter, and if you want to keep some to study them you can easily do so by putting them in a closed jam-jar with some bits of damp blotting-paper or paper towel and breadcrumbs. They are generally no trouble and don't multiply very rapidly, but if there are lots of them they may sometimes make a nuisance of themselves by attacking starched linen or the dried glue in a book binding.

The female silverfish lays only about 20 eggs during her lifetime. They are placed in cracks and holes and are left to look after themselves. From the eggs the youngsters emerge not as grubs but as perfectly formed tiny silverfish. They take 6 months to reach their adult size, and like all insects grow by shedding their outer casings from time to time.

Silverfish have many close relatives living near the house. One likes to be out of doors and is often seen on rocks on hot days. Another, the *ant silverfish* may be found in the house and in ants' nests. Some silverfish, called *spring-tails*, have a sort of sprung tail folded beneath their abdomen. By using this tail they can jump rather like fleas. Spring-tails can often be found in gardens, flower-pots and damp cellars. Two species of true silverfish can be found throughout the year in Britain.

The Clothes Moth

The adult clothes moth has a body 1 cm long and brown or silvery-grey wings fringed at the edges, but despite its name it *doesn't* eat clothes. When it becomes an adult moth it has already chewed all the holes in woollen sweaters that it is ever going to chew, for it is the moth's larva, its caterpillar, that does all the chewing!

Clothes moths are true moths, and members of the great insect family *Lepidoptera*, which includes both butterflies and moths. They are secretive creatures and prefer to shuffle along on their legs rather than fly. The male is more active than the female and is the one usually to be seen flying. These insects existed long before man began making woollen clothes for himself and originally made their homes in birds' nests and similar places, feeding on feathers and fur. They can still be found there and around owl droppings, another source of fur and feather scraps. Clothes-moth caterpillars do not attack cotton or any man-made material.

There are two different kinds of clothes moth. The caterpillars of both sorts spin silk to form a sort of mobile home while they munch their way through life, moulting from time to time and eventually hardening into a pupa from which the adult moth emerges. The caterpillars of the *case-making clothes moth* make tubes of silk and fibre within which they live and which they carry about with them. *Webbing clothes moth* caterpillars make loose silken webs as tiny protective tents over themselves where they feed.

Moths on my old sweater

The old-fashioned way of keeping

clothes moths away from clothes was to place 'moth balls' containing a strong-smelling substance called naptha in drawers containing clothes. Nowadays various sprays and strips that give off a vapour are used. These kill both the adult moth and the caterpillar, and are very much better than moth balls at protecting woollens and furs from attack.

The clothes moth is one of the commonest insects that attack clothes and stores in the home. There are also many others that join the zoo in the house from time to time. The larvae of the *fur beetle* eat fur, wool and flour. The *carpet beetle* has furry larvae known as 'woolly bears' that chomp the fibres of rugs and carpets. The larvae of the *larder* or *bacon beetle* stuff themselves on dried meat and animal skin, while the shiny brown larvae of the *mealworm beetle* love cereals. The grubs of the *black weevil* go for carrot leaves in the vegetable rack. Even though they may sometimes be a nuisance, none of these insects carries disease.

A clothes-moth caterpillar's tube

Clothes-moth caterpillars

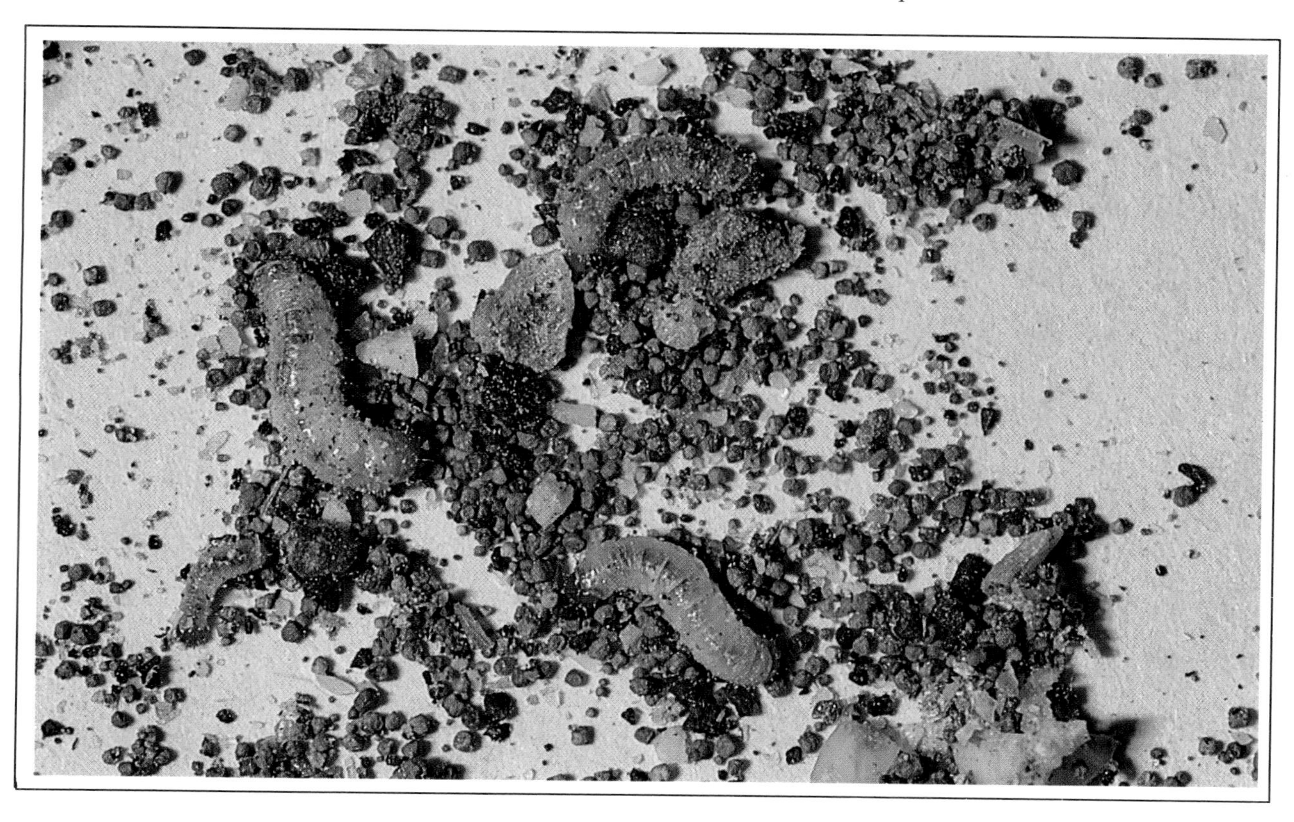

The Dust Mite

Every zoo includes a number of species that can be seen in large numbers, often with their young. In the big public zoos, for instance, you can often see large groups of rhesus monkeys, lions, gazelles and some kinds of bird. So what about in the zoo in the house? Several of the creatures we are looking at in this book may well outnumber the humans in the house, even when you have visitors. But there is one kind of animal that makes its home in the house in numbers running into tens or even hundreds of thousands. This creature is the mite, a tiny relative of the spider.

The Gospel of St Mark in the Bible mentions a poor widow who threw two mites into the collection-box at the temple. The mites in that case weren't a pair of creepy-crawlies that the widow kept in a jam-jar, but the very smallest coins. The mites that live in your house are the very smallest arthropods (creatures with joints in their legs), and some are too small to be seen without a microscope. Like the spider, they have 8 legs and belong to the group of arthropods called Arachnids. There are many species of them, and they can be found all over the world, even in the frozen regions of the Arctic and Antarctic, where few creatures can survive. Some live on land, some in fresh water and some in the sea. Some of them live as parasites on animals or plants for either the whole or just part of their lives (parasites are creatures that live off other living things without doing them any good). The largest

A monster? No – a dust mite

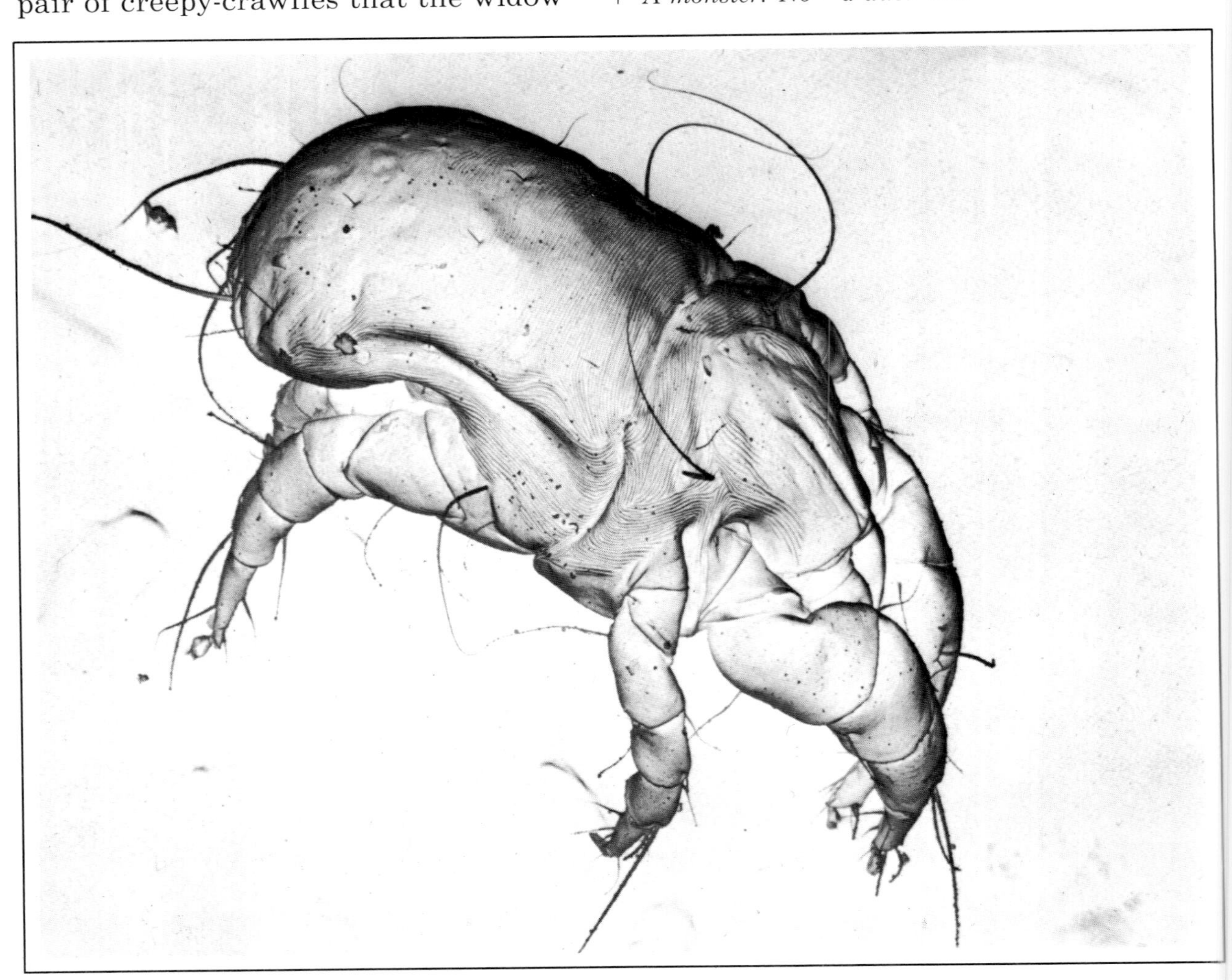

The widow's mites were small coins

species of mite are found in the tropics. These mites can be up to 1.3 cm long and are covered with crimson velvety hairs. The bright colour warns other creatures that they are nasty to eat. One sort of mite spins webs and is sometimes called the 'money spider'. With a good magnifying glass or a microscope you may find in a drop of pond water the round red or green fresh-water mites. They have long hairs on their legs to help them swim. When you are down on the beach, look for the seawater mites that creep about on seaweed.

In the garden soil or in leaf-mould under trees (especially in pine forests) there are thousands to the square metre. The mites that live closest to the surface have darker-coloured and firmer bodies than those that live deeper in the ground. Some of these mites eat rotten wood, while some prefer fungi.

Parasitic mites cause a skin disease called 'mange' by feeding upon the skin scales and sucking the blood of animals; one of the commonest, which you can see without a microscope, makes its home in the ears of the domestic cat. Mites that attack plants produce a sort of 'mange' on buds, stems or leaves, often doing a lot of damage to fruit-trees. One species is responsible for the galls or swelling often found on blackcurrant bushes during May and June. The conspicuous red galls found on sycomore and maple leaves during the late summer, with up to 1000 galls on each leaf, are produced by mites. So are the pale green galls that can be seen on the leaves of blackthorn bushes throughout the summer months.

You can be sure that there are

thousands of mites going about their business in your house. *Cheese mites* may be in the larder inspecting the cheese rind. *Book mites* spend their days between the leaves of old books feeding on bits of paper and dried glue. *Grain mites* are often found feeding on cereals in the kitchen, and in grain-stores and from time to time attack man, nibbling at his skin with their tough mouth-parts to cause a type of rash known as 'grocer's itch'. But the commonest creature in your household zoo is likely to be viewed in the *dust*! No house can ever be free of dust — it is a rich grey mixture of material fibres, hairs, bits of soil, wood and a thousand other substances, and skin-scales of the sort that are continuously shed throughout life by man and other animals. House-proud mothers hate dust and are always trying to get rid of it. To dust mites, however, it is a snug, dry forest. Because they too are too tiny to be seen without a microscope, dust-mites have only one major enemy, which is not an animal at all but the vacuum cleaner!

Take a pinch of dust, put it on a microscope slide, drop on a little paraffin or cooking oil, place a coverslip on top and look through the lens. With a little searching you should have no difficulty in spotting a mite among the tangle of fibres, flakes and other bits and pieces. The dust mite has a rounded unsegmented, bag-like body with four pairs of not very long legs, pointed at the end. It has a mouth with feeding-

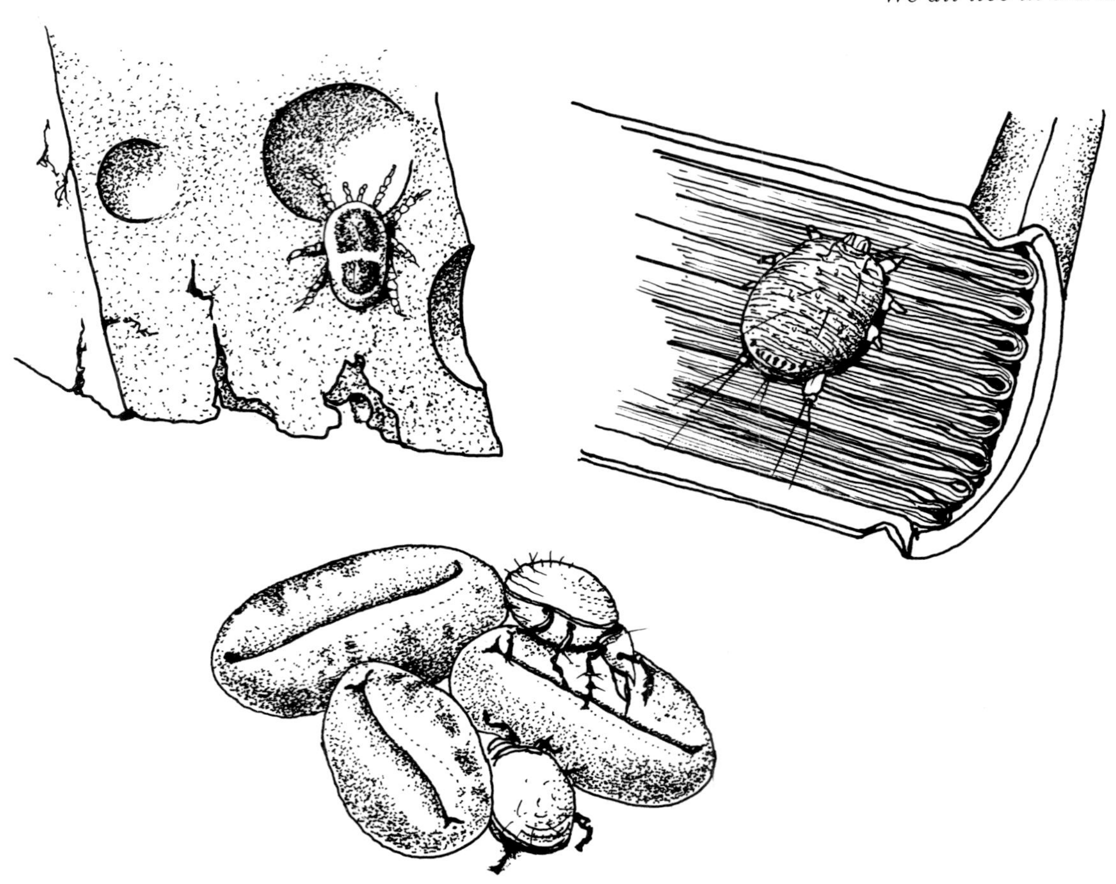

Cheese mites
Grain mites
Book mites
We all live in the house

parts that look like pincers, and segmented feelers. It breathes by means of air-tubes in the skin, like some other Arachnids and insects. There are male and female dust mites. The females lay eggs that hatch into 6 legged larvae. These then pass through a further 3 stages before becoming 8-legged adults. Some mites can reproduce from eggs that have not been fertilized by a male.

Although mites that are not parasitic do not tend to cause much harm to man, it has been found that some people are allergic to dust mites. If there is a lot of dust in the air, then when they breathe in the dust – and the dust mites – they find it very difficult to breathe. The symptoms are rather like those of the disease called asthma.

When you are next asked to do some dusting around the house, don't complain about it, but think of it as a useful way of keeping the zoo in the house from becoming overcrowded!

A scorpion, the mite's cousin

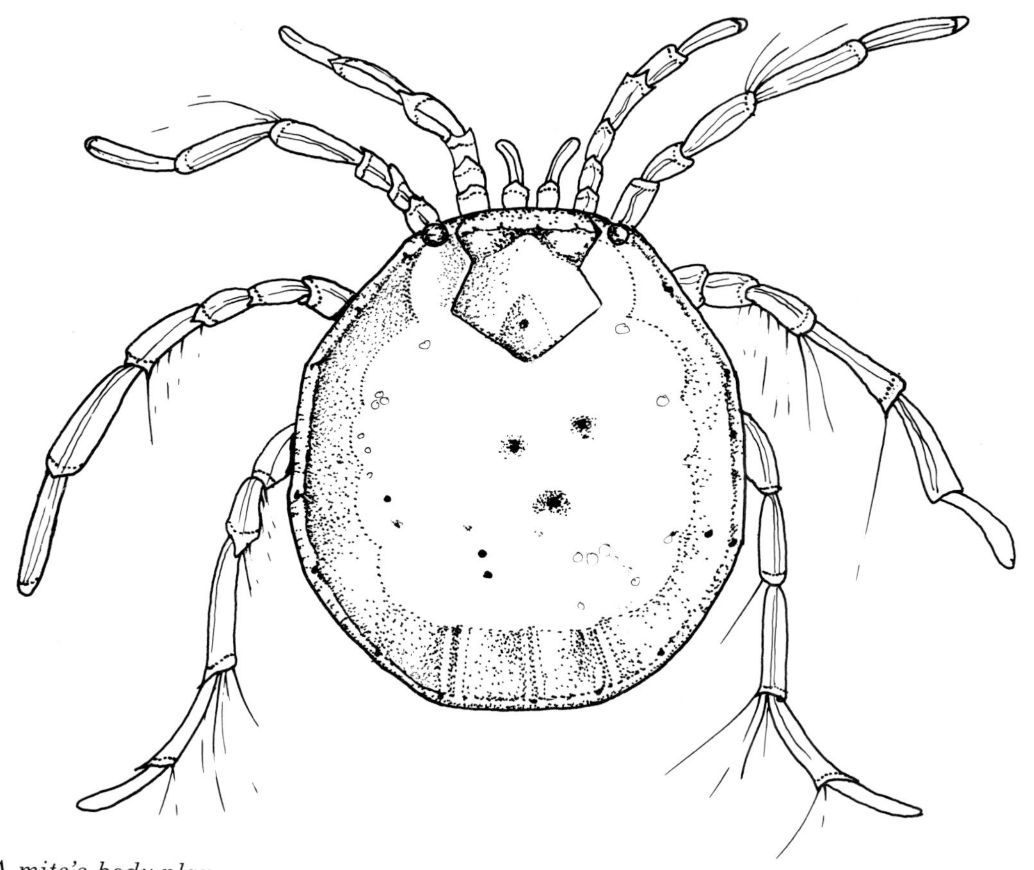

A mite's body plan

The Woodworm

When is a worm not a worm? Answer: when it is a beetle!

I expect that on old timber beams, door-posts and antique furniture you have seen the small holes that are the entrance to tunnels bored by woodworms. However, although these holes are often seen, the creature that makes them is seen much less often. The culprit is in fact not a worm at all but the larva of a beetle.

Outside the house, many species of beetle larvae specialize in drilling tunnels in wood, eating the plant material and drinking the sap as they go. Some bore only in wood of living trees; some prefer dying or dead timber; and some like their wood to be rotting. In Britain, for example, the bright-green *musk beetle* is sometimes found on willows, where its larvae like to do their mining, and in the jungles of South America big *longhorn timber beetles*, which can be up to 20 cm long, produce huge larvae that bore into and feed upon balsa wood. These larvae are dug out by the local Indians, who think them very tasty and eat them raw or roasted. Another interesting beetle is the ambrosia beetle. Its larvae drill tunnels and chambers in wood, and the adults plant fungus gardens in these to provide food for their larvae. It is this special food that gives the beetle its name: 'ambrosia' is the food of the gods in Greek mythology and here means a rare and tasty dish! (There are also ambrosia ants, who grow gardens of

The damage to timber is caused by the larvae of the woodworm beetle

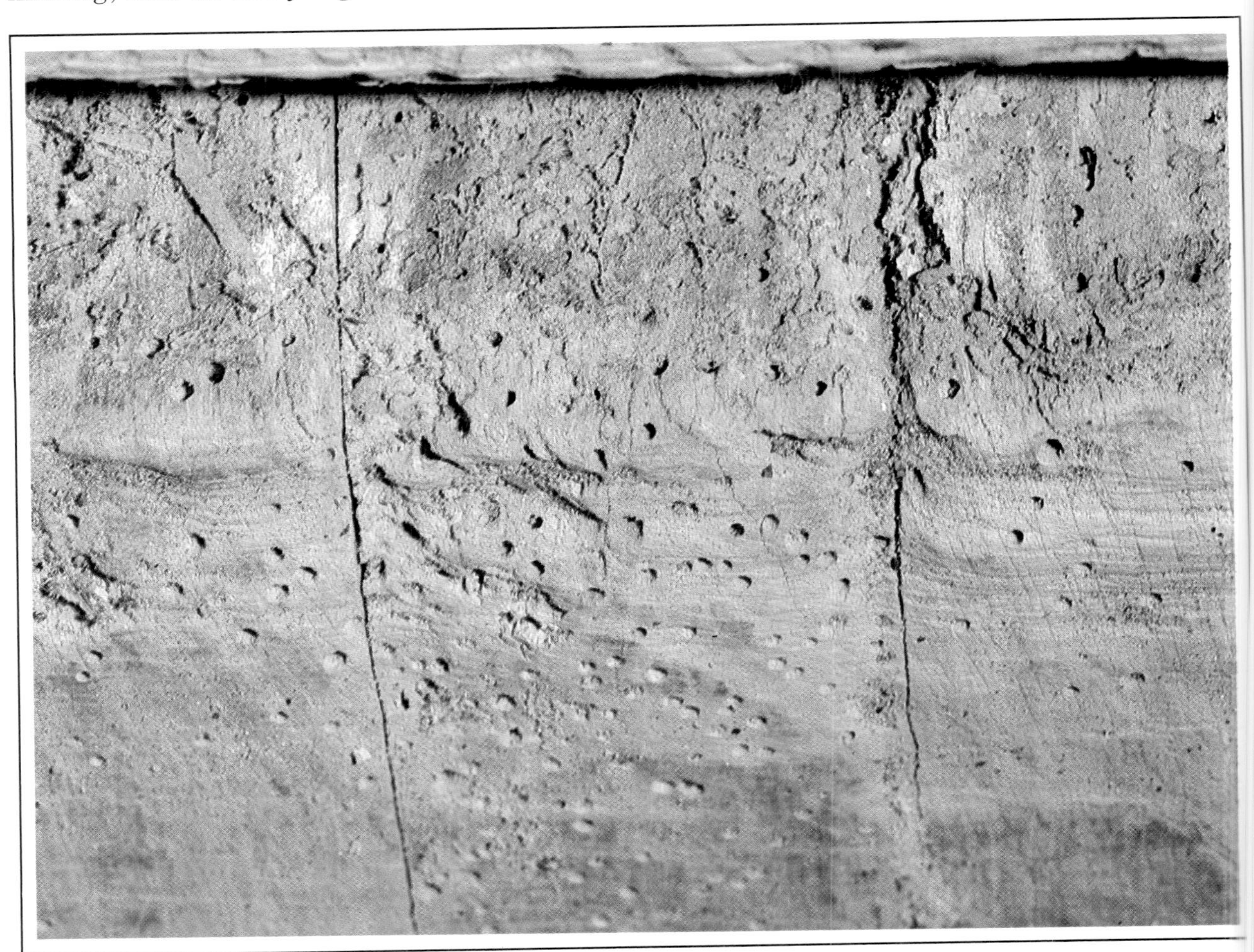

fungi in their underground nests to provide dinners for themselves and their young.) Ambrosia beetles grow their fungi on beds of wood-shavings, which are manured by the insects' droppings! One type of ambrosia beetle has the nickname 'tippling Tommy' because of its habit of drilling holes in wine or rum barrels! (A tippler is someone who drinks a lot of alcohol.)

Out of doors the larva of the *woodworm beetle* attacks deciduous trees (trees that shed their leaves in autumn), but indoors it is the commonest and most destructive insect pest that attacks woodwork. It attacks soft woods over 20 years old and hard woods more than 60 years old. Other insects that are sometimes up to the same mischief indoors are the *death-watch beetle*, which favours old oak, and the *powder-post beetle*, whose larvae go for soft wood with the sap still in it and push out dust powder behind them as they drill their holes. (The woodworm

A woodworm beetle

The larva in his tunnel: on the increase in your home

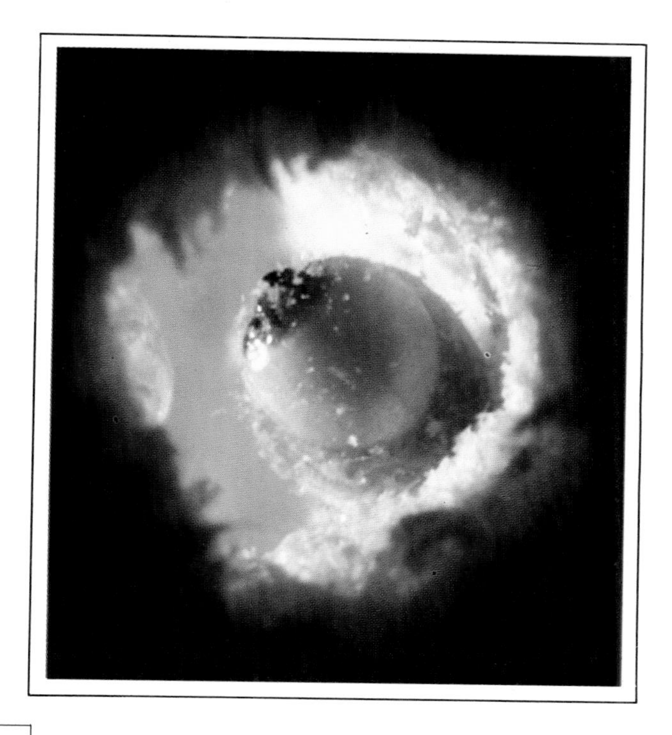

beetle's larvae push out small pellets of wood dust.) *Lymexylon* is a beetle whose larvae prefer to burrow in very hard wood.

Three quarters of all British homes are being attacked by the larvae of the woodworm beetle at this very moment! The British population of this species has been steadily increasing since 1945. The adult beetle can fly and has a narrow black body. It lays its eggs in cracks on the surface of timber, and once the larvae have hatched they drill tunnels through the wood, feeding as they go. If they are not stopped, they will eventually turn the beam or chair into a crumbling shell and a pile of powder. One piece of furniture containing woodworm can infect every other piece in the same room within 6 months, so it is important to act fast if woodworms are discovered in your home!

The death-watch beetle, often found in old churches. Its ancestors arrived with the timber from which churches were built

Death-watch beetles are more commonly found in old churches, where there is often a lot of ancient oak. The beetle came into the building when the timber was originally put in place, and, if there are still beetles at work there, it is likely that they are descendants of the original beetles rather than new arrivals. Such beetle populations may therefore go back hundreds of years. They have seen bishops and priests come and go, and have steadily munched on through countless christenings, weddings and funerals.

The name 'death-watch' refers to the ticking noise made by the beetles, particularly at night. They make this noise by banging their heads on the floors of their tunnels! The banging is a sort of mating-call. The beetles can't hear, but pick up the vibrations through their highly developed sense of touch. In the past the sound of the death-watch beetle was thought to mean there was soon going to be a death in the house. In tropical countries, the larvae of some wood-eating beetles are so noisy when they eat that the sound of their gnawing deep in a tree-trunk can be heard from several metres away.

Just as public zoos and safari parks often have problems with uninvited lodgers such as pigeons, sparrows and rodents, the zoo in the house can well do without the woodworm beetle and its tunnelling relatives.

Body plan of a woodworm beetle

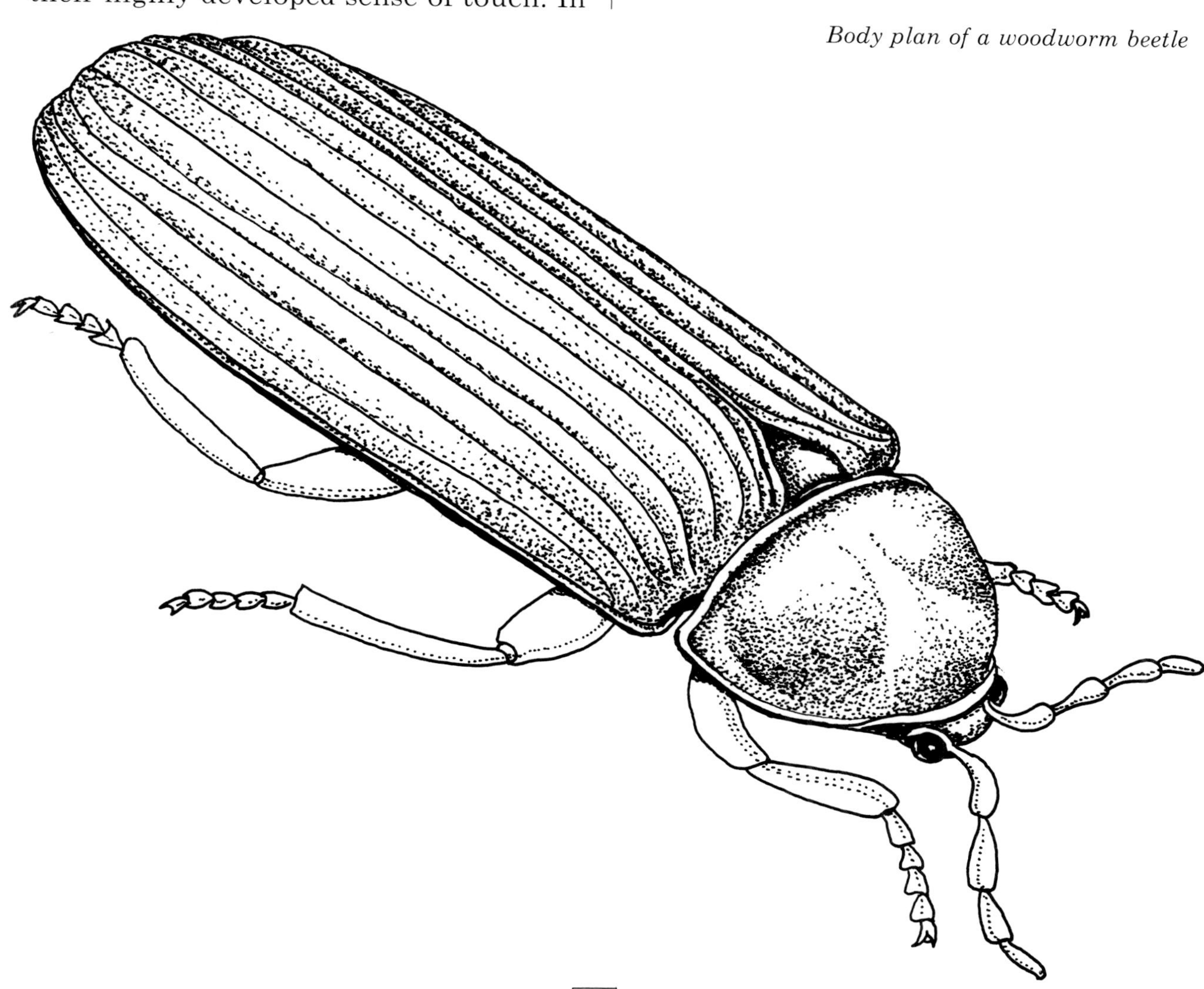

The Ant

The writer of the Book of Proverbs in the Bible was right when he said, 'Go to the ant, thou sluggard, consider her ways, and be wise'. (A sluggard is a lazy person.) We shall do just that, for one of the truly exotic animals in the modern zoo in the house is *pharaoh's ant* – a tropical ant that was imported by accident and is now common throughout Britain, though it can survive the cooler climate only inside heated buildings, particularly in towns. 'Pharaoh' was the title of the kings of ancient Egypt, and pharaoh's ant seems to get its name from the pharaoh in the Bible story about the plagues of Egypt (though the story says nothing about ants!)

Ants are social insects who live in well-ordered communities. They have an abdomen attached to the front part of the body by a narrow stalk, and antennae that have an 'elbow bend' in them. Sometimes they have strings on the tip of the abdomen. Ants are one of the most widespread groups of insects, and are common in nearly all parts of the world. Each colony of ants consists

Male ant *Female ant*

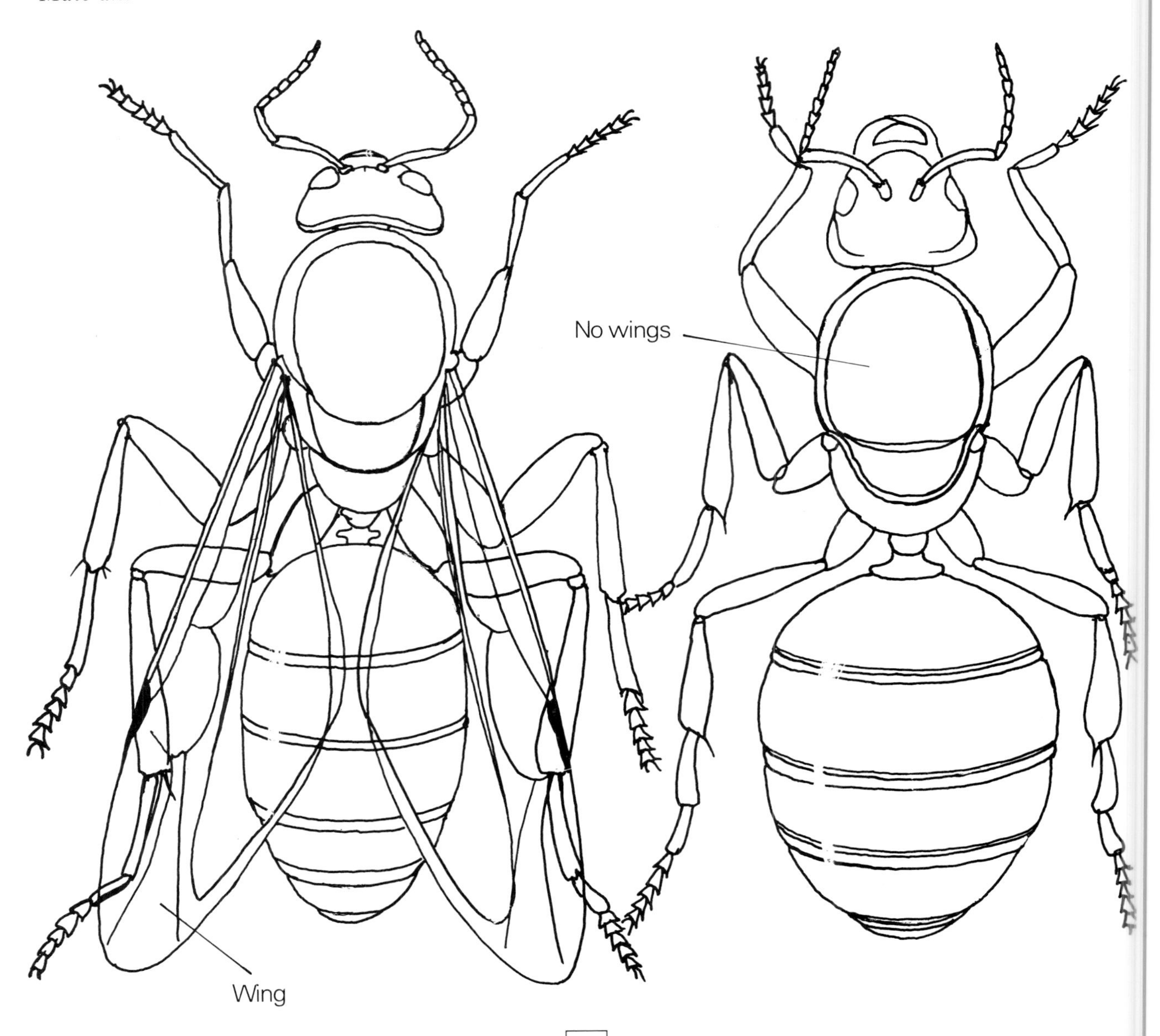

Anatomy of an ant's nest

of a queen (or several queens) and a large number of workers. The workers (females who cannot lay eggs) are usually very much smaller than the queens (females who can), and are entirely wingless. The males are winged and appear only at the time of swarming, when they fertilize the queens and quickly die. The females are at first winged, but lose the wings shortly after swarming and before they raise their first brood of young. Each ant species is thus composed of females, males and workers. The more primitive ants are carnivores who hunt prey, while the more specialized and abundant types are mainly or entirely vegetarian, some even growing fungi in their nests as food for themselves and their brood.

Many ants nest in the ground, while others live in hollow twigs or burrow into wood. Some build nests of 'cardboard' made from chewed wood and saliva, and some tropical ants construct nests of leaves spun together with silk. Some ants have a powerful sting and some can't sting at all. Some ants in the tropics spend most of their time on the march and only settle down to raise their brood. These kinds are highly predatory, often travelling in great armies and destroying every living thing in their way.

The queen lays her eggs in the nest, and the workers take great care of

Ants 'milking' aphids

them. If the colony is threatened, they take them somewhere safer. The larvae that hatch from the eggs are legless, helpless grubs that have to be fed by the workers. Their bodies are often provided with hooked bristles, and these serve as handles that the workers can use to move them about, either singly or in bundles. When fully grown, the larvae change into pupae, from which the adult ants emerge.

Around 50 species of ant live in Great Britain. The *black garden ant* is the only native British ant and is often to be found inside the house, although it does not live there. The *wood ant* builds mounds and constructs its nests inside. A single nest can contain up to a third

A seething colony of ants

of a million workers. The *blood-red ant*, which is found only in small areas of south-eastern England and north-eastern Scotland, makes slaves of other ants. The *jet-black ant* is found mainly in the south and 'milks' aphids of the sweet honeydew that they secrete. The *Argentine ant* is a tiny thin, black ant only 2 mm long. It came to Britain from the tropics and, like pharaoh's ant, can

Red ants with their eggs

only survive in heated buildings.

Pharaoh's ant is about the same size as the Argentine ant, but yellow or reddish in colour. It can now be found in almost all parts of the world. It makes its nest in the walls or beneath the floors of heated buildings. Though only 2–2.5 mm long, these little ants wil often gang up to fight and drive off or actually kill and eat insects much bigger than themselves. They prefer to feed on sweet foods and some kinds of cooked meat, making long trails between their nests and the goodies they have found. Although generally regarded as a pest, pharaoh's ant can be useful. It feeds on some household pests such as that unpleasant creature the bed bug.

Like other ants, pharaoh's ant is amazingly talented. It can learn and remember things, and can do amazing calculations when using the sun as a compass to find its way. Pharaoh's ants can see and recognize one another from a distance of around 2 cm and, like the wasp, can tell where the sun is even when it is hidden by cloud. This is because they are sensitive to light that humans cannot see.

Ants have a language of smells that they use to communicate with each other. At least 10 different scent 'words' used by ants have been deciphered by scientists. The ants leave a trail of scent

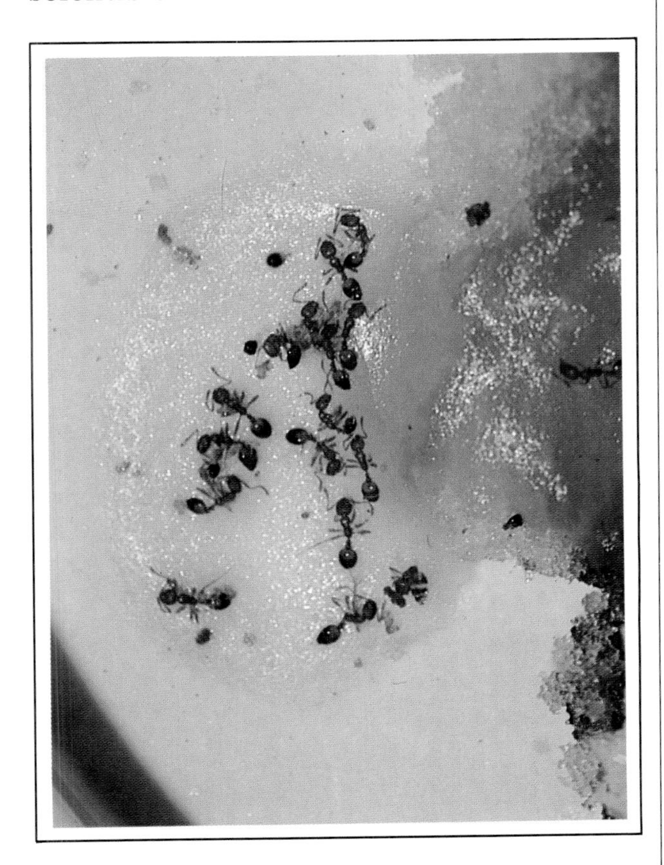

Pharoah's ant on jam pudding

by pushing the sting out of their abdomen and using it to squeeze a scent gland. A fine trickle of liquid is deposited, like ink running from a nib of a pen. The trail left is a series of arrow-shaped marks rather than an unbroken line, which would be wasteful of the precious liquid. Scent pathways laid by ant 'scouts' show the way for the marauding armies of *driver* and *army*

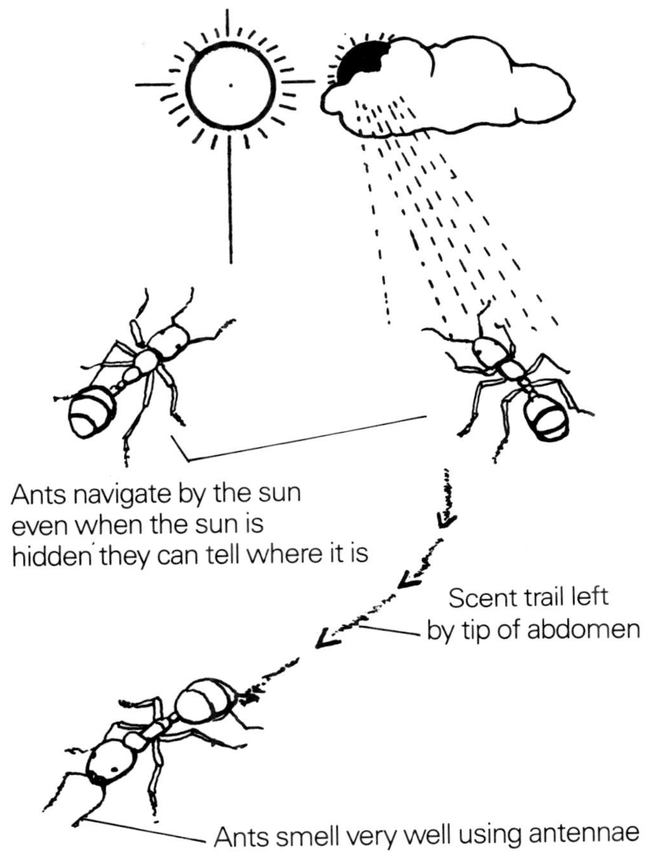

An ant's senses: they navigate by the sun and 'smell' very well

ants that sometimes march across Africa and South America.

Ants also produce special alarm smells and there are even smells released by dead ants which stimulate their living companions to hold a sort of funeral service, carrying out the body and burying it in an ant 'cemetery'. It seems that by mixing scents and varying their strengths and the pattern of their scent trails ants can communicate a whole series of different messages. Some ants also use sound, by knocking their heads on stones, cracking their mouth-parts together or using a groove on their bellies to make a strumming noise.

Discover the animals which
live in your town

The Rat

Although some scientists believe there were no rats in Britain before the Middle Ages, and that they arrived on the ships of soldiers returning from the Crusades in the Holy Land (what is now Israel), they probably lived in Britain long before that. These first British rats were *black rats*, which came from the Far East and whose relatives still live there. They often live in the roofs of people's houses, for they are good at climbing.

The black rat, a clever climber

Black rats took a liking to travelling by ship and in the days of the early Spanish and Portuguese explorers were often eaten by sailors when other food had run out. On one voyage made by an English merchant ship, nearly the whole crew fell ill with the dreaded scurvy, caused by not eating fresh food. One man, however, remained fit and healthy. When asked how he had managed this, he said that he had eaten raw, freshly killed black rats!

The black rat was certainly in Britain by the fourteenth century, when it spread the disease known as the Black Death – or, rather, the rat carried the flea whose bite passed on the germ that caused the disease! The black rat is now rare in most parts of Britain, having been pushed out by the *brown rat*, which arrived around the year 1720, probably from China or Central Asia. Brown rats are bigger, stronger and more aggressive than black rats, and they got rid of them by eating them and their food-supply. Brown rats don't like any competition, even from mice; where there are brown rats you will rarely find mice. People used to believe that the brown rat first came to Britain on board the same ship as George of Hanover, who became King George I, and for this reason they called the animal the 'Hanoverian rat'. Another theory was that the rat came to Britain hidden among the timber on Norwegian ships. That is why the Latin name of the brown rat is *Rattus norvegicus*, meaning 'Norwegian rat'. It is estimated that in the United States there are 200 million black and brown rats, and that they cost the country £1000 million a year (£5 for every rat) in spoiled crops. One report said that rat hairs had been found in nearly a third of samples of various tinned food products.

Because they have hair and feed their young on milk, rats are true mammals, but they are also rodents. 'Rodent' comes from the Latin word meaning 'to gnaw', and all rodents have one pair of upper gnawing teeth (unlike rabbits, which have two pairs and are not rodents, being more closely related to hoofed animals such as cattle and deer). Over 40 per cent of all mammal species on earth today are rodents. There are

The brown rat

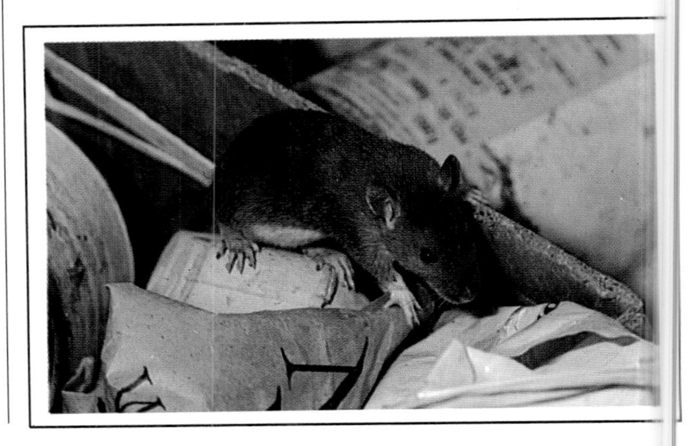

The rat, a typical rodent

dozens of different species of wild rat in the world.

What is the difference between a rat and a mouse? It is not just a matter of size, for there are small species of rat and large species of mouse! To scientists, 'rats' and 'mice' are simply names given to various species within the animal family called *Muridae*. Rats have more rows of scales on their tails than mice have. Rats have 210 or more, but mice never have more than 180.

Apart from the brown rat and the black rat, there are *water rats*, with large flattened tails that they use to swim with, *swamp rats, tree rats, field rats, jerboa rats, bamboo rats* and *kangaroo rats*, to name but a few. Jerboa rats have long hind limbs and tufted tails and are found in north Australia. Africa has giant rats 75 cm long. In the Solomon Islands in the Pacific you will find a *woolly rat*, while New Guinea is the home of *Mallomys*, a very large species with gorgeous long hair speckled with white. *Anisomys* is another rat that lives in New Guinea. It is creamy-coloured all over except for a dark base to its tail. The rarest rodent in the world is probably *Swarth's rice rat*. Only 4 have ever been seen alive (in 1906), and that was the last anyone knew of this creature until 1966, when the skull of one that had recently died was found. The home of this creature (if it is not yet extinct) is on James Island in the Galapagos Islands, off South America.

Disease-carrying wild rats should not be confused with the tame rats kept as pets, which are clean and gentle creatures. They are lively, easily handled and cheap to feed. White rats especially are very common as pets, but there are many other colours to choose from. An acceptable rat should be very much of a busybody, always on the go and rather nosey. It should look clean and healthy, having sleek fur with no thin or bald spots, and it should not mind being handled. The tail must be smooth-skinned and completely undamaged, and there must be no sign of lameness when the rat moves about. If you wish to buy a tame rat, go to a good pet shop or look through the magazines in which rat-breeders advertise. In this way you should be sure of obtaining a good animal.

Rats are very successful creatures. They are tough, breed rapidly and are very adaptable, which is why they can be found in nearly all parts of the world. In the wild, rats generally do not live very long – usually only a few weeks or months. Tame rats tend to live much longer – up to 3½ and sometimes even 5½ years. Rats are alert, with well-developed senses of sight, hearing and smell. They communicate with each other mainly through smells produced by their scent glands and through the various sounds they make. They have in-built homing-instincts but are almost certainly colour-blind, seeing the world only in black and white.

Like most small rodents, rats drink very little water; this is because their bodies obtain almost all the water they need from the food they eat. The bodies of larger animals, including humans, also obtain some of the water they need from their food, but they need far more water than rats and so drink a lot too. If you keep rats as pets, though, you must make sure that they always have fresh clean water, because tame rats may not be as hardy as their wild cousins.

Some species, such as the kangaroo rats, are very good at jumping. They have specially sensitive ears, which control balance as well as hearing (to be good at jumping you need a very good sense of balance, so that you don't fall over). Kangaroo rats live in the desert, where it is very useful to be able to hear well too. South American fish-eating rats and water rats are first-class swimmers. Some rats, such as the wild black rat, are very good at climbing. The black rat developed from tree rats, and can dash along telephone wires better than any tightrope-walker. The brown rat can climb too, though many people think it can't; but it is not as clever at it as the black rat is.

Rats can eat 10 per cent of their body weight in food every day, but spoil a much larger amount when they are active in food-stores. 100 rats eat around a ton of cereal grain in a year. In other countries rats damage crops of sugar cane, rice and oil palm. It's little wonder that man thinks of wild rats as a serious enemy and does all he can to get rid of them. He uses all sorts of poisoned baits to kill rats, but often rats quickly become immune to the poison or learn to avoid the bait.

An extraordinary character called Jack Black was Royal Rat-catcher to Queen Victoria. He advertised himself as 'Rat and mole destroyer to Her

Jack Black, the royal rat-catcher, in his official uniform

Majesty'. His official uniform was made up of white leather breeches (trousers that only reach to the knee), a green coat, a scarlet waistcoat, a gold-banded hat and a belt across the shoulder onto which were fixed four rats made of pewter. Not only did Mr Black catch and kill rats and other pests, but he also bred and sold pet rats, especially 'pied' or 'variegated' rats (rats with patches or blotches of different colours). Some were fawn and white, some black and white, some red and white, some black, white and red, and so on. All these rats were bred from the brown and white rats. Mr Black sold many of his pet rats to ladies, who kept them in cages designed for squirrels.

Rats have not always been thought to be bad things. In olden days many people thought they had magical powers, knowing about the future and able to warn people of danger and disaster. It was also claimed that rats would react to certain kinds of music and magical charms. The famous Pied Piper of Hamelin is said to have emptied the town of Hamelin in Germany first of its rats and then of its children in the year 1284. (There is a poem about him by Robert Browning.) If you go to Hamelin today you can still see the story told in marvellous model figures that appear from behind a clock every hour.

In 1953 a British magazine stated that there was still a rat-charmer working in Cornwall – a man who could attract rats by whistling. The animals would come running to him, and he was then able to pick them up and dispose of them.

The Pied Piper of Hamelin

The Fox

It is always a thrill when I am driving along at night and my car headlights pick out the sleek red-brown shape of the fox slipping into a hedge or through a garden gate. It's a common sight at night in our towns nowadays – often in roads far from the open country. Reynard the fox is becoming, much to my delight, a town-dweller. One thing for sure is that he is safe from the huntsman when he's roaming the town! And what a wonderful creature this master of cunning, this handsome member of the dog family, is. Intelligent and clever, he has long been known for his cunning: in the Bible, for example, Jesus likens King Herod to a wily old fox.

There are 21 different species of fox. Our friend the *red fox*, the only type of fox to be seen in Britain outside zoos, is also the most widespread and adaptable of all the dog-type animals. It can be found from the Arctic Circle to North Africa, from Asia to Central America. Other types of fox are found in a much smaller area. They include *Blanford's fox* of Afghanistan and the mountains of Iran in Asia, the *crab-eating fox* of South America and the *pale fox* of North Africa. Some species, such as Blanford's fox and *Colpeo's fox* of the Andean mountains in South America, are endangered species. The rarest foxes are the North American *swift fox* and the *small-eared dog* (really a fox!) of South America.

What is a fox? It is a small member of the dog family that has a pointed muzzle, large ears and a bushy tail or 'brush'. With its muzzle it can smell about 1 million times better than a human can; its large ears give it very sharp hearing; and its tail is used for balance when running and for signalling to other foxes.

Although the *bat-eared fox*, which lives in the African plains, lives mostly

Reynard the fox, member of the dog family

on termites, the rest, including the red fox, will eat all sorts of things: dead sheep, rabbits, rodents, birds, fish, frogs, insects and worms, plus fruit, mushrooms and even rosehips! Sometimes fruit can make up 90 per cent of the diet. Foxes enjoy grapes too: the Song of Solomon in the Bible speaks of 'the little foxes, that spoil the vines'. Foxes also have a habit of storing food by burying it. They do this especially with birds' eggs. When they need this food they rely on their nose rather than their memory to find it. A fox can smell out a bird buried 10 cm deep in the ground when passing 3 m away, and it can smell out eggs buried 5 cm deep if it happens to pass within 50 cm of them. Luckily for them, young rabbits buried in the sand by their mother before she goes off looking for food are almost always missed by a passing fox. This is because they have even less of a scent than eggs have.

Good ears, eyes and nose of a hunter

Some foxes actually live in the town and bring up their families there. Gardens and parks and waste ground offer lots of places where a fox can make a den. Other foxes are 'commuters': like people who travel into

A fox's incredible sense of smell

A fox cub close to a city centre

the city every day from the countryside, they live in the country and only visit the town. These foxes usually come into the town at night, in search of the easy pickings to be had round man's rubbish dumps, dustbins, gardens and back-yards.

The fox in the town is no threat to the pet dogs and cats that it may meet on its travels, but it is sensible to make sure that your rabbit-hutch is strong and that the wire netting on the front isn't broken or loose anywhere. The fox has adapted quickly to life in town: there are lots of places for dens, and the fox has found lots of food that it can happily eat. Most important of all, in the town the fox is safe from hunters, gamekeepers and farmers, and modern farming methods have made it difficult for lots of creatures, including foxes, to find enough food.

A fox's home is its den, which may be an enlarged rabbit-hole, an old badger's sett, a dried-up drain or a space beneath a garden shed in winter. In summer red foxes normally rest above ground where there is plenty of cover (trees, bushes or deep undergrowth). They live alone except in the mating season, when they form groups of up to 6 foxes: one male or 'dog fox' with a number of females or 'vixens'. All females in any group are relatives. When they have grown up, male cubs move out of the group and can travel away as far as 250 km. Even when part of a group, a fox still tends to hunt alone, over territory that can be as little as 8 ha or as much as 2000 ha. A fox claims a territory for its own by leaving droppings or drops of urine around the border.

Smell is important for foxes as a way of communicating with each other. They have glands at the base of the tail, on the lips and between the toes that produce a sweet, musty smell. Foxes also signal with their bodies (for example, by the way they hold their ears or tail) and make a variety of different sounds. Barks, yowls, screams and whines have their own special meanings.

Foxes are good at digging burrows, though species such as the bat-eared fox, which does a lot of digging to find the termites it lives on, are better at digging than red foxes. Red foxes catch their prey by a sort of jump called a 'mouse jump'. The fore-legs rise high and then fall straight down to trap the victim beneath the paws. The nose comes down on the prey straight afterwards.

Foxes mate in January or early February and one litter of cubs is produced each year, usually in March. The number of cubs in a litter averages about 4. Sometimes 2 or more vixens share a burrow and will suckle one another's cubs. A vixen's milk is richer than the milk that a human mother feeds her baby, with 5 times the protein and about twice the amount of fat. When the cubs are older, the dog fox helps feed the youngsters by bringing home dead prey.

Although foxes do sometimes raid hen-pens and poultry-yards, they are *not* a great pest and certainly not so bad that they need to be hunted. The animals have long been admired for their cleverness and courage by country folk and there are many traditional beliefs associated with them. People believed at one time that witches could turn themselves into foxes, and as late as the end of the last century the inhabitants of Kirtlington in Oxfordshire spoke of a local woman who transformed herself in this way. A fine fox was often seen near her house, and was often hunted, but never caught. Once the hounds were so close behind it that it seemed impossible for it to escape, but the hunted animal made a sudden turn and rushed into the woman's house. When, a few seconds later, the huntsmen followed it, there was nothing to be seen but the 'witch' sitting quietly by her fireside. Or so the story goes! In Wales it is thought lucky to meet a single fox but unlucky to see several together. In many parts of England it is still thought that foxes get rid of their fleas from time to time by taking a piece of sheep's wool in their mouths and wading with it into a pond or river until only their noses are above water. The fleas, to escape drowning, rush onto the wool and the fox then lets it fall into the water and float away. Some folk say that the fox will use a bunch of dry grass rather than wool.

And do you know what a 'fox's wedding' is? When a sudden shower of rain falls while the sun is still shining, country people say that somewhere a fox is being married.

On patrol near London's Tower Bridge

The Wasp

Late summer and autumn is the time when wasps come to town in search of sweet, ripe fruit. We all recognize the wasp, and most of us have been stung by one. The wasp that we all know is the *common wasp*, but it is only one of about 10,000 known species.

Wasps are stinging insects that, unlike bees, mainly hunt other insects, which they feed to their young. Some are solitary and usually live alone, while others form colonies or social groups. Social-wasp colonies are founded by a single queen. At the end of the season all members of a nest die except the queen, who, after being fertilized so that she can lay eggs, goes into hibernation. The following spring she founds a new colony. A typical wasps' nest consists of a queen, a large number of female workers (who cannot lay eggs) and a smaller number of males. The 3 forms are very alike in colour and markings, but the queens are much the biggest. Males have 7 segments to their abdomens and 13 joints in their antennae; females (queen and workers) have 6 segments to their abdomens and 12 joints in their antennae.

The common wasp

A wasp's nest in a roof

Common wasps are about 2 cm long, with the familiar black and yellow markings. They live in colonies in beautifully constructed nests made of paper. The paper is composed of fragments of wood chewed and mixed with wasps' saliva. The nests are usually underground in a burrow left by some small animal such as a mouse, but they may be built in the rafters of a building. I have had one on the outside of my garage, under the eaves (the

A nest beautifully built of paper

pointed part under the roof). Inside the colony there are combs of cells arranged in flat layers – unlike bees' honeycombs, which stand up on end. You don't see many wasps about in spring and early summer, because the worker wasps are busy hunting and killing insects such as aphids (greenfly), flies and sawfly caterpillars to feed to their larvae. The adult wasps feed on a sweet saliva produced by their larvae. Sometimes, if the insects killed are rather big, the wasps cut them up into pieces to make it easier to take them back to the nest. Most of the insects that wasps attack are pests, so they can correctly be understood as friends of mankind.

In late summer and autumn, with no more larvae to feed and so no supplies of larva saliva to feed upon, wasps go looking for fruit, jam and other sweet things, often in our houses. But all except the queen die by the time winter arrives. Sometimes you may see the queen wasp coming indoors around October or early November looking for a place to hibernate. She may well settle in the fold of some hanging curtains.

Other social wasps in Britain include the *hornet*, which can be up to 3 cm long and is the largest British wasp. The hornet is quite rare now that so many old trees where it used to nest have been cut down. The *red wasp* has an orange-red abdomen and nests under old leaves, logs or matted grass. The *cuckoo wasp* is so called because it makes no nest but lays its eggs in the nest of the red wasp. The *German wasp* lives in the ground and can be distinguished from the common wasp by the three black dots on its face. The *tree wasp* nests in roof spaces, gaps in walls and hollow trees.

Most British wasps do not live in colonies but lay their eggs in small

A German wasp, with 3 spots on the head

nests together with a supply of food in the form of a living but paralysed fly, spider or grub. Some lay their eggs in the bodies of living creatures such as caterpillars or even the larvae of other wasps or bees. When an egg hatches, the larva starts eating the other creature from inside, but is clever enough not to kill it straight away, leaving until last the parts that keep it alive. Some species of wasp lay their eggs on greenfly and others, such as the *Ichneumon fly* (actually a wasp), lay them on butterfly caterpillars, with perhaps 100 eggs in each caterpillar. *Mason wasps* make nests in the loose cement of walls and place a paralysed caterpillar next to the egg. *Potter wasps* live on sandy land and actually construct a pot of 'clay' made from grains of sand stuck together with saliva. The pot is fixed to a plant, an egg and a paralysed caterpillar are popped inside, and a lid is sealed into place. A female potter wasp lives only 2 weeks and makes several pots during that time but dies before any of her larvae hatch out.

The larvae of *wood wasps* burrow in trees. Some other wasps listen for these larvae with the 'ears' on each of their 6 feet and also sniff them out with their incredibly sensitive antennae. They then bore a hole in the wood using a special long drill on the end of their abdomens and deposit an egg within the larva's body. One kind of wasp larva lives inside oak leaves and produces the brownish bumps that are called spangle galls. Another species of wasp then comes along and lays its eggs in these galls to feed upon its relative's larvae!

Unlike bees, wasps have unbarbed stings that can be withdrawn to use again. Stings are used to kill or paralyse prey and also as a defence against

A parasitic wasp that preys on other insects

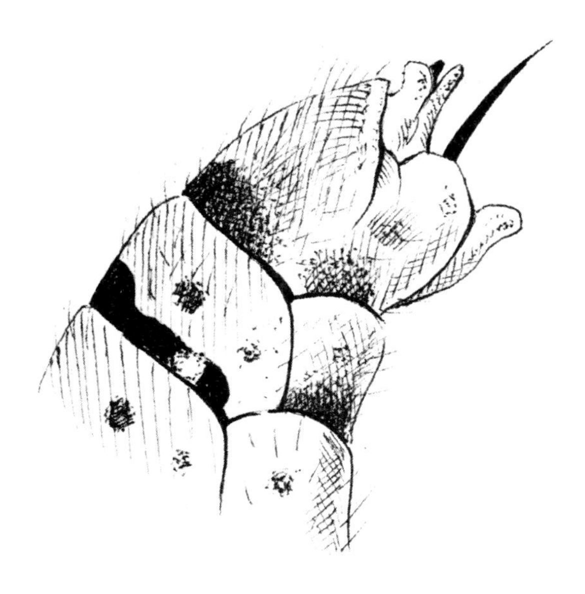

The unbarbed sting of the wasp

enemies. The very large yellow and black *Geting wasp* of Sweden gives an extremely painful sting. The sting of a wasp is a hollow needle that injects a liquid containing a mixture of chemicals, some of which cause swelling and burning and others of which can put an insect to sleep or cause it to have convulsions (uncontrolled jerking movements). Sometimes formic acid, the stuff that ants secrete, is also present.

When disturbed by a possible enemy, wasps squirt out an alarm substance. This hits and marks the enemy's body and the smell spreads out and warns other nearby wasps, making them highly aggressive. This is how a colony of wasps can become quickly roused to anger. Like bees, social wasps use scent as an important means of communication, and can find their way about with great accuracy, thanks to a sort of in-built sun compass. Even when it is cloudy they can tell where the sun is, because they are sensitive to light that we cannot see. Wasps have also got a good memory for landmarks.

There is no need to be frightened by the wasp. Respect this fascinating creature, treat it patiently and let it go about its business and it'll do you no harm. The only time of year when wasps are likely to sting people is at the end of summer, when the colony has no queen and has only a few days to live.

Wasps spread the alarm – by chemicals

The Cockroach

La Cucaracha, the Spanish name from which we get 'cockroach', sounds quite jolly. Besides being the name of the insect, it is also the name of a Latin-American dance. Certainly the cockroach is one of the oldest types of insect and one of nature's cleverest designs, but there isn't really anything very jolly about this common pest of town and cities.

Cockroaches are flat-bodied insects with long thread-like antennae and shining, leathery body-casings. They are active at night. They originally came from the tropics, but they have spread throughout the world by being carried from country to country in ships' cargoes. There are around 3500 known species of cockroach, but only 6 are found in Britain. As these insects come from warm countries, in Britain they make their homes in heated buildings, mines and sometimes rubbish dumps, which become warm and damp as the rubbish rots away. Cockroaches love kitchens, coming out at night when all is quiet to eat scraps of waste food. They will eat an amazing variety of things, including bones, paper, clothes, books, shoes and dead insects. They even eat other cockroaches. Above all they love bread and other starchy foods.

An unwelcome gathering of cockroaches

It may be that friendly germs living inside their intestines help them to digest their food. Cockroaches must have water and can survive a long time on water alone. The big problem about cockroaches is that they spoil far more food than they actually eat, and spread diseases on their feet and in their droppings. What is more, they make a horrible smell.

Cockroaches themselves do not suffer much from disease. This is mainly because they coat their bodies with a thin oily film containing an antiseptic chemical, which kills germs. But they do suffer from mites which live on their bodies and tiny worms which live inside them. Surprisingly, cockroaches are quite resistant to nuclear radiation and could be the only form of life to survive a war with nuclear bombs, even though they do fight a lot among themselves!

Their flat bodies are perfect for squeezing into tiny cracks, and with their long legs they can run fast. They can run up walls and across ceilings using claws on their feet if the surface is rough, and sticky pads on the legs and feet if the surface is smooth. Adults, but not young cockroaches (called 'nymphs'), can easily climb up glass.

Female cockroaches lay an egg-case that contains 10–16 eggs. The eggs

Cockroaches have long antennae for smelling

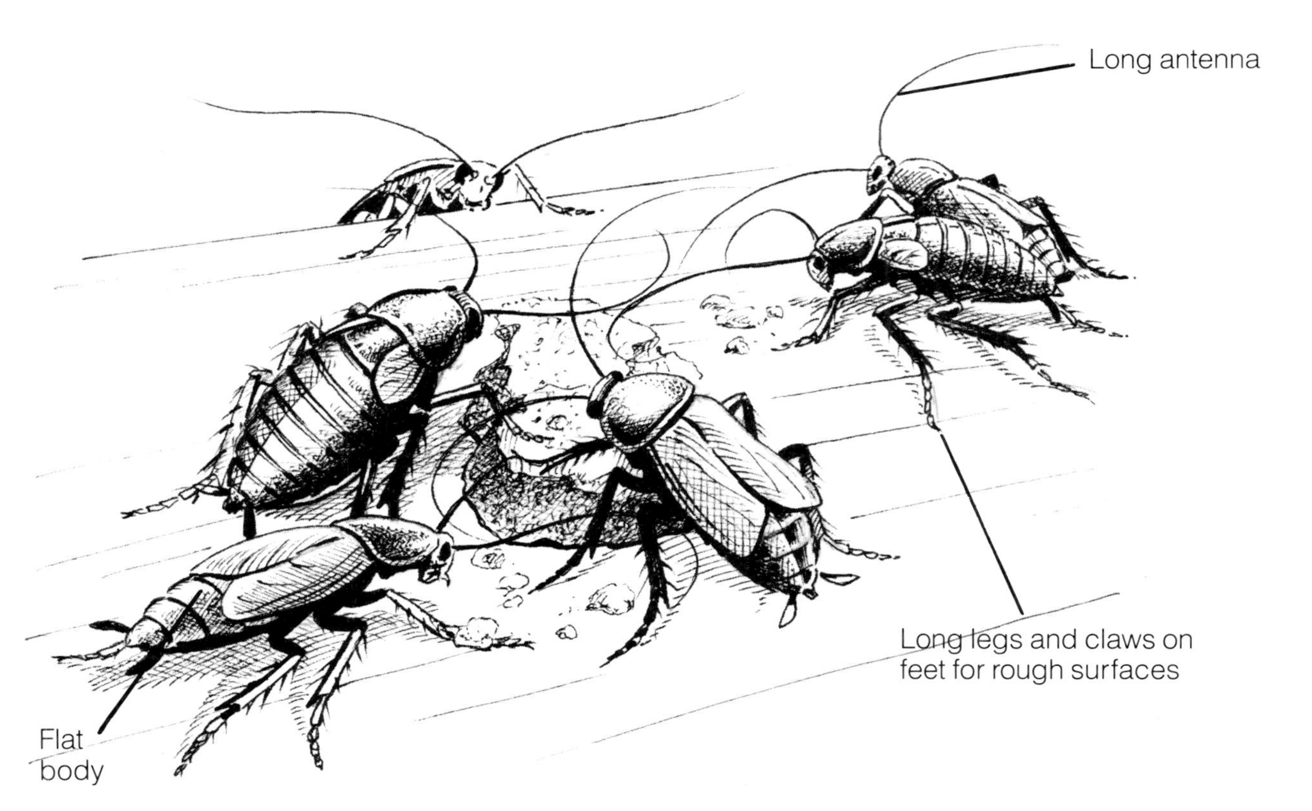

hatch in 40–45 days, depending on how warm it is, and the babies are not grubs or caterpillars but nymphs, which are tiny cockroaches without wings. After moulting several times, the nymphs become adults. The adult *common cockroach* lives for about a year.

Some cockroaches, such as the common cockroach, have lost the ability to fly. The common cockroach is red-brown to black and up to 2.8 cm long.

Cockroaches have big, complex eyes and their antennae give them a keen sense of smell. They use smell to pass messages. Some tropical species are beautifully coloured and much more handsome than the cockroaches found in Britain. Big tropical cockroaches, which flutter or parachute with their wings rather than flying in the usual way, may have a wingspan of up to 13 cm.

One of the famous lost goldmines of the Americas is called 'the Cockroach'. It was hidden deep in the jungle and the gold was easy to get at, but it was full of cockroaches. Millions of them

The body-plan of the cockroach

swarmed throughout the mine, forming a thick moving carpet on the walls and making such an abominable smell that nobody could stand it. If you are *very* fond of cockroaches and can find the mine again, the gold is yours!

Cockroaches' bodies are coated in antiseptic

The Moth

Like butterflies, moths are insects belonging to the huge *Lepidoptera* family. *Lepidoptera* means 'scale wings', and their wings are indeed covered by rows of tiny little scales arranged in rows and pegged on just like roof-tiles. But moths are less popular than butterflies, mainly because they usually are more active by night than by day. The English poet Shelley refers to 'the desire of the moth for the star' and we know how moths are attracted to bright lights and can easily perish in their fascination for a candle-flame. An old Japanese legend relates how the moths first fell in love with the night-fly. To get rid of the moths, the night-fly cruelly told them to go and fetch fire for her. The blind lovers flew to the first flame to obtain the fire, and few escaped alive.

There are over 80,000 species of *Lepidoptera* and 2000 of them can be found in the British Isles. Moths differ from butterflies in several ways: they are generally duller in colour; they have stubby furry antennae without blobs on the ends; and when they are at rest they usually spread their wings out instead of folding them together, as butterflies do. The life of a moth is similar to that of a butterfly: the eggs are laid on a plant which the caterpillars can eat when they have hatched, and after

The legend of the moth and the night-fly

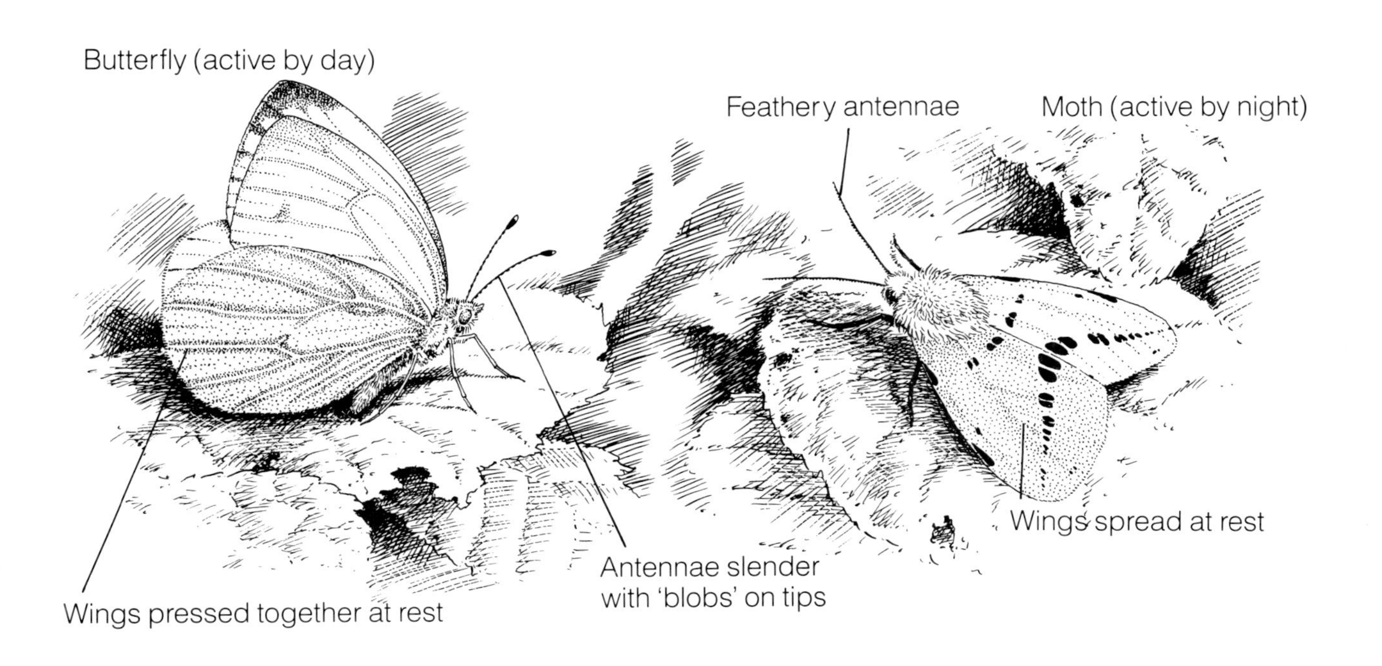

Differences between moth and butterfly

several moults the caterpillar stops growing and becomes a pupa or chrysalis. Wrapped up in its cocoon, it slowly changes again and eventually emerges as an adult moth.

Moths have a number of enemies, and one of the deadliest is the bat, a mammal that can fly in the dark and find its prey by using sonar beams – high-pitched sounds that the bat sends out as it flies along and that tell it when there is something in its flight-path. If there is a moth within range, the bat's bleeps bounce off the moth and the echoes return to the bat's highly sensitive ears. From the signal it receives the bat knows just where the moth is. But the moths have developed their own anti-bat night-flying defences! They try to fly silently and have soft furry bodies that soak up sound and send a very weak signal back to the bat. To cut down the noise caused by their wings as they fly through the air, some night moths have grown a fringe of fine hairs, 2 mm long and 0.007 mm across, that smooth out and silence the movement of the air. Moths also have ways of telling when a bat is approaching. They have special 'ears' on both sides of the thorax, near to the waist. At a range of about 30 m the 'ears' pick up the first bleeps of a bat's sonar. At once the moth changes its flight-path and tries to avoid being picked up by the bat's sonar, for, although the bat is much faster than the moth, it needs to be within about 7 m before it can pick up the echoes of its sonar bleeps and tell where the moth is. To overcome the moth's defences, the bat does not fly in a straight line but reels about in what seems a very clumsy way. In fact the bat is not clumsy at all, and its flying-curves are designed to deceive the moth's anti-sonar. The first

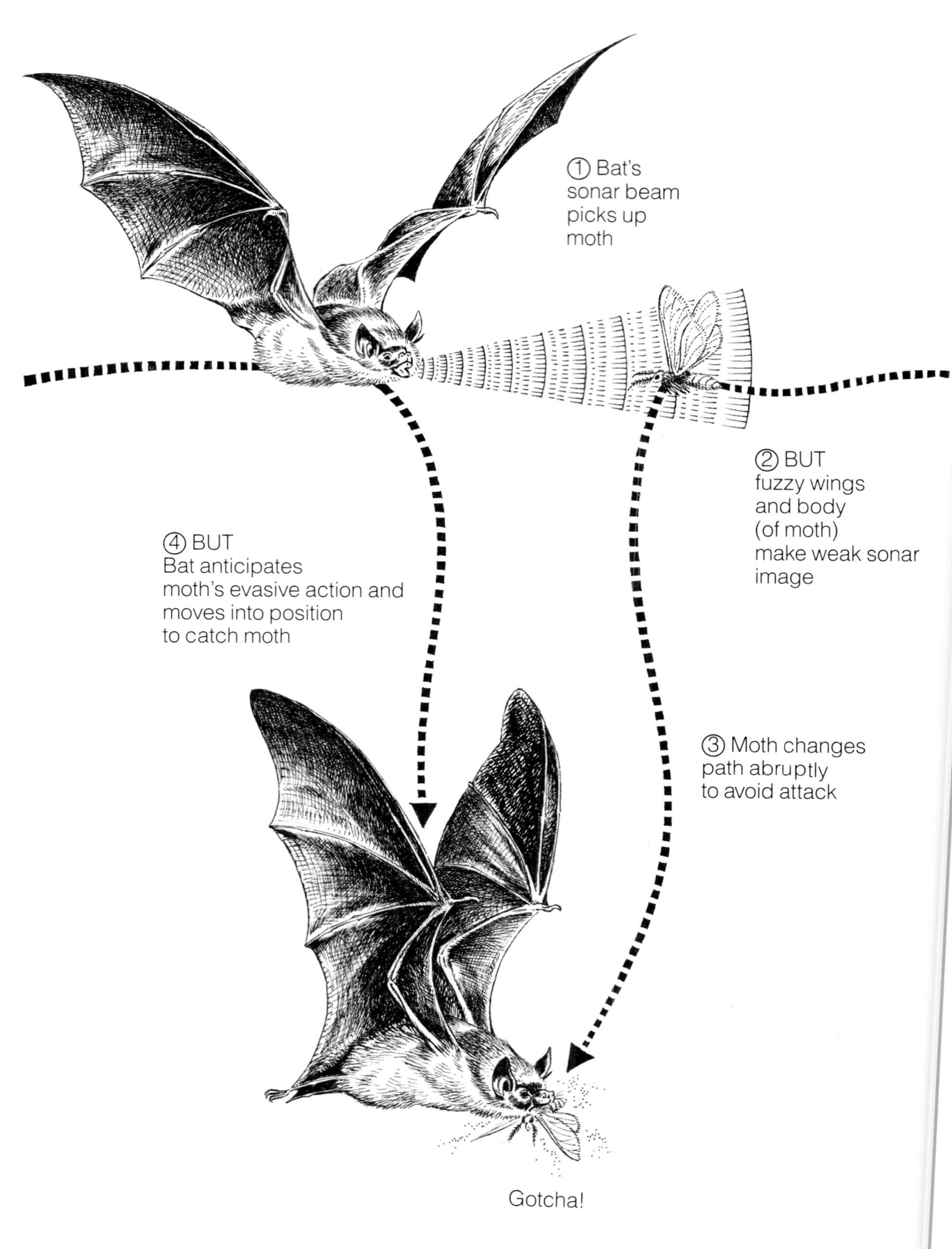

A 'dog-fight' between bat and moth

A poplar hawk moth

echoes that a bat receives from a moth when it is within sonar range are about as loud as a fairly quiet car engine!

Once they know a bat is within range, some moths simply fold their wings and drop to the ground, but bats know all about that and have learned to change course so that they can still manage to catch half the moths that try this trick. Many moths are amazing acrobats in the air – looping-the-loop, spiralling and even falling behind the bat and trying to keep there in fights as skilful and tense as one between two fighter planes.

Moths are very good at telling which direction a sound is coming from, but they are completely tone-deaf, unable to tell the difference between high and low notes. Some moths produce sounds as soon as the bat's sonar finds where they are. These very high-pitched insect noises warn the bat that the moth is very smelly or tastes disgusting, so as to put it off the chase. The sound is made by a horny grooved plate on top of a sound-box (which makes the sound carry) where the third pair of legs join the body. Some clever moths make this warning sound when they are not really smelly or bad-tasting at all, and the bats avoid them in just the same way as they avoid insects that they really would want to spit out.

Moths can find their way by the stars. They have eyes that are very sensitive to starlight and they can see and recognize at least as many stars as man can. Like butterflies, moths have an incredibly sharp sense of smell. Male *silkworm moths*, for example, can smell females from many miles away. To do this they use their antennae, which have lots of tiny branches, and on these branches are an amazing total of 40,000 nerve-cells. These nerve-cells can sense the tiniest amounts of chemical in the air.

The largest moth found in Britain is the *death's-head hawk moth*, a very rare visitor from Africa. Its wings measure up to 13 cm across. The largest known moth is the *great owlet moth* of Central

Scarlet tiger moths at rest

A cream-spot tiger moth

and South America, with an enormous wingspan of up to 36 cm. Compare that to the smallest moth, *Stigmella*, which lives in the Canary Islands and is only 2 mm across with its wings fully stretched!

A moth common in British towns, as well as in damp places in the countryside, is the *poplar hawk moth*, whose wings are various shades of brown with a reddish patch on each of the hind wings, close to the body. This patch can be seen when the insect is disturbed and raises its fore-wings. The caterpillar feeds on the leaves of the poplar, willow and aspen trees.

I think that the prettiest species of moth in Britain is the *elephant hawk moth*. It is common in south and central England and is often seen on June evenings feeding on petunias, soapwort and valerian. This moth is most easily found in places such as rubbish tips and waste ground where rosebay willowherb grows. The female lays her eggs on this plant and the caterpillars feed on it.

Common in town: the cinnabar moth

Moth caterpillars are usually far more beautifully marked than the adult insects. Some have similar colours and patterns to the plant on which they feed, making them difficult to see. Some are brightly coloured as a warning to birds that they taste nasty, or have strange designs or peculiar extra bits designed to frighten off or trick attackers. Some have rows of hairs that can cause rashes when touched. In the United States, *puss moth* caterpillars secrete a poisonous liquid that can make children ill. Even more sinister is the *vampire moth*, which lives in the Far East and bites and sucks blood from water buffaloes, deer and other forest animals. However, none of the British moths is in any way dangerous.If moths come into your house, make them welcome, protect them from naked flames and be gentle when you decide to put them outside.

An elephant hawk moth

The garden tiger caterpillar

The Starling

I share my house with a group of talkative, busy and charming friends. We've been together ever since I moved in, and even as I write I can hear one of them talking outside, while another is working on the garden. We get along very well and I don't make a fuss about the spots of what looks like purple fruit-juice that they deposit on my white car every day: it's easy enough to clean off. I refer of course to the handsomest of our town birds, the starling. Starlings are the fifth most common visitor to the bird-table and, along with sparrows, arrive to dine in large groups. They often nest under the eaves of the house – always in the same place at the corner above my study. They sing to me from the roof-top, and use the television aerial as a concert platform where they can show off by fluttering their wings while they perform. Their song is a mixture of trills, chuckles and clicks, with occasional sharper calls that seem to say 'cheer, cheer', often followed by more little chuckles. The starling is a very common bird in Britain, and each

A starling outside my study

A starling in summer

winter the birds that live in Britain all the year round are joined by visiting starlings from continental Europe. The starling is a bigger bird than a sparrow but not quite so big as a thrush, and has a summer coat of black that gleams with flashes of blue and green and is dotted with white spots. In the summer the beak is yellow. In winter the coat seems less glossy, the white dots are more obvious and the legs are a darker yellow-brown. Young starlings are a greyish brown.

As a group starlings are one of the most successful of all our bird species. Unfortunately they are very bossy birds that push other species, such as woodpeckers, out of their homes. There are 106 species of starling in the world, and some of them are very useful at controlling insect pests. For example, the *wattled starling* and *rose-coloured starling* are great gobblers of destructive locusts in hot countries. The *European starling*, though, sometimes does a lot of damage to crops of young corn, olives and grapes. In Britain starlings are only a nuisance in the centre of big cities, when they visit them in huge flocks. Lots of money is spent trying to get rid of them, but the starlings keep coming back.

A starling in winter

Away from city centres, starlings do a lot of good. They eat lots of insects, including some important pests, and they also help the farmer by perching on the back of grazing cattle or sheep and picking off flies, lice and fleas. As you can tell from its name, the tropical starling called the *ox-pecker* does this useful job for oxen. Some foreign species of starling are very fussy about what they eat. The *Brahminy starling*, for example, collects pollen and nectar using a brush-like tip on the end of its tongue. The starlings of Britain, however, are not fussy at all, and will eat all sorts of things. They like to feed in flocks, particularly in the winter. Their long, straight beaks are very strong and can deal with many different types of food. They especially like poking about in lawns and short grass. This poking-action is very good for lawns, letting them 'breathe' through the tiny holes made by the starlings' beaks.

More and more starlings are living in our towns and cities. They are birds who love to do things together, and flocks of up to 1 million of them have been seen in some city centres. They are noisy and aggressive, but it is a wonderful thing on a winter's evening to see a cloud of them following one of their regular flight-paths to their night roost. They come into cities because it is always warmer there than outside. Among their favourite places are Leicester Square in London and the common in the middle of Boston in the United States. In these places some trees are completely covered with starlings.

Starlings usually fly in straight lines. Every autumn great flocks of them fly

Evening in London: coming in to roost

from Scandinavia to spend the winter in northern France, southern England and Ireland. These migrations have been well studied by scientists. They have caught over 1000 of these travellers, put a tiny ring on their legs to say where they were caught and then let them go again so that scientists in other countries who find them can tell where they have come from and study their migration-patterns. In this way scientists have proved that starlings hatched in Scandinavia are born with an in-built map of Europe. They know instinctively which direction to fly in to reach their winter home. Older birds who have migrated before can remember landmarks and in addition know how to find their way by the sun and the stars. They even have a magnetic compass in the form of tiny pieces of iron in their heads! Like the compass used by sailors and explorers, this starling compass can tell where the magnetic North Pole is and so help the traveller know which way to go.

When in flight, dense flocks of starlings wheel and turn without any bird bumping into another one. No one knows how they do this. Could it be that they have a sense similar to the bat's sonar, so that they can always change direction before bumping into something? If they have, scientists have not yet found out about it.

Starlings don't only build nests under the eaves of houses. They may nest in a hole in a tree or a cliff or up in an attic The nest itself is a loose, rather untidy construction of dried grass or straw lined by feathers, and in spring the path outside my study is littered with bits of grass and other rubbish dropped by starlings as they go about building their nest. Eggs are laid in clutches of 4–6, and 2 clutches are laid each year, between April and May. The female incubates the eggs, while the male often goes off to mate with a second female. Some females behave like cuckoos and lay their eggs in the nests of other starlings. Incubation takes 2 weeks, and 3 weeks after a hatching the chicks are ready to fly. The male will help feed the chicks of his first mate, but he usually leaves his second mate to feed her chicks herself.

There is very little difference between town starlings and their cousins who live in the countryside. It is just that, like many sparrows, rats and foxes, a large number of starlings have realized the advantages of town and city life. There is food all the year round, and shelter and warmth in the colder months. Many different kinds of bird live in town, and they brighten up the town for many people who live there.

A starling feeds its young

Home is a tree-hole

The Sparrow

The sparrow is a cheerful, harmless little bird, the commonest in Britain. It can be seen almost everywhere, but most people think it dull or boring and take no notice of it at all. In fact the sparrow is as well-bred and interesting a creature as any bird of paradise or monkey-eating eagle – and has proved far more successful as a species.

Strangely, although sparrows are so harmless, in many European folktales and legends they are said to be wicked. A Russian tale relates how when Jesus was in the Garden of Gethsemane all the other birds tried to stop his enemies from finding him, but the sparrows betrayed him by chirruping loudly around the place where he was. They also were cruel to him when he was on the cross. Because of this, the tale says, sparrows are cursed, and their legs are tied together by invisible bonds so that they can never run but only hop.

Our little friend in winter

Sparrows belong to the family of birds called *Weavers*, of which there are 143 species spread across the world. Most true Weavers live in Africa and are,

Sparrows were said to be no friends of Jesus

unlike the sparrows, often very brightly coloured creatures, mainly yellow and red. Some, such as the *golden-palm weaver* and the *golden bishop*, are very attractive little birds. As you can guess from their name, Weavers make their nests by weaving them. Often the entrances are guarded by tunnels, which can be up to 60 cm long.

Although sparrows are unhappy in cages, they do all like to be close to humans. *House sparrows* rarely nest far away from houses. There are 8 species of sparrow in the world that usually nest in buildings. Some species, such as the *tree sparrow* in Britain and the *yellow-throated sparrow* in other countries, nest in trees, though in Britain tree sparrows will nest in buildings when there are no house sparrows about. *Rock sparrows* and *pale rock sparrows*, which are not found in Britain, nest – of course – in rocks! The *hedge sparrow* or *dunnock*, a shy little bird that lives in hedges, is not really a sparrow at all but a member of a family of dull-coloured birds called *Accentors*.

The commoner of the two British sparrows and the one that lives in town is the house sparrow. It is the third most common visitor to our bird-tables. It is small and stubby, and its beak is designed for eating seeds. All true sparrows are seed-eaters, though the house sparrow is quite happy with bits of bread and household scraps. House

The hedge sparrow or dunnock

Lunch-time

I sit here when it rains

sparrows love sunflower-seeds. Don't forget to put some out in winter!

House sparrows are bold little birds who are often cheeky enough to throw out house martins and take over their nests. The male is easily distinguished from the female by his bolder markings and the black 'bib' under his throat. House sparrows fly noisily, making a whirring sound. They usually fly in straight lines, but over longer distances they tend to rise and fall. Sociable and often quarrelsome, they love to be in groups and will roost together in winter, often using their old nests to keep warm. Sometimes on a winter's night a tawny owl will swoop towards a group of roosting sparrows, and catch one in mid-air as the little birds take fright and flutter down to the ground.

Sparrows are not good at singing. The song is simply a lot of chirps and cheeps, repeated over and over again, but they are not the slightest bit embarrassed about it. From the way they sing their hearts out, they seem to think they are nightingales!

Watching sparrows is really fascinating. Take time to watch them scolding, squabbling, competing, searching for food, courting and

A refreshing bath – of dust

The courtship of sparrows

cleaning themselves up and exercising their wings. If you put a shallow tray about 4 cm deep and 20 cm long and wide in your garden (or dig a pit the same size) and fill it with very fine sand or ashes, you will be able to watch your sparrows having a dust-bath. If you are really lucky, a wren may come along too.

House-sparrow nests are rather untidy. They are made of dried grass, bits of paper and any other material that the birds can find, lined with feathers. It is charming to watch sparrows courting. The males often collect in groups, and compete to attract the females by showing off. They puff out their chests and hop around the females with their wings held low. 2 or 3 clutches of 3–5 white eggs with small brown and grey markings are laid between April and August. The female incubates the eggs for 2 weeks, sometimes with help from the male. The young sparrows are fledged (ready to fly) 2 weeks after hatching.

Don't turn up your nose at the humble sparrow as you see it picking up crumbs in the street, its feathers dark with dirt or soot. Sparrows are wild birds that have chosen to live among us, and they are as interesting to watch as any rare bird. They are also one of the easiest species to watch, because they are so used to people. The sparrow long ago found that life close to man suited it very well. Because it is not too fussy, it found plenty of food in the town. As a seed-eater, it was quite happy to eat bread, which is made from seeds (the cereal grains from which flour is made are seeds). The town also offered lots of warm, dry places to shelter. Many species could not live in the town because they would not find their special food there or the right sort of places to rear their young. Like the rat and the cockroach, the sparrow did not have these problems, and that is why it was able to fit in so well.

The Pigeon

The second most common bird in towns and cities is the pigeon. In Trafalgar Square in London the flocks of pigeons are a tourist attraction and you can buy food to give them. In other places they are considered to be a pest, and poisons, sticky pastes and electric wires are used to stop them from perching on the roofs and buildings. Often you will see notices telling you not to feed the pigeons, but you can still see them in the streets and shopping-centres of old and new towns, keeping an eye open for little old ladies with bags specially filled with grain or dried crusts, or for any scrap that someone might happen to drop.

Lots of people see pigeons every day of their lives but know next to nothing about the history of this common bird. The pigeon I am talking about is the one scientists call the *feral pigeon*, the species seen mainly in towns. It is not a truly wild species, but comes from pigeons that were bred from the wild *rock dove* as racing and carrier pigeons or simply for show – just as pet rats were bred from wild rats. Carrier pigeons are pigeons that can be trained to fly straight home from wherever they are released, carrying messages rolled up in a small tube attached to the leg.

There are several wild members of the pigeon and dove family that live in Britain. ('Pigeon' and 'dove' are just different names for members of the same family.) The *wood pigeon* lives in the countryside and is famous for its call of 'coo-coo-coo-, coo-coo'. The *stock dove* also likes the country, and the *collared dove* has begun to move into town. It first came to Britain from continental

Trafalgar Square's famous pigeons

A wood pigeon

Europe in 1955, and loves grain. It has spread very quickly.

There are around 300 different species of pigeon in the world. Some are very rare and some have recently become extinct because of man's thoughtlessness. Pigeons can be found in every part of the world except Antarctica and the Far North, and include such exotic species as the *Victoria crowned pigeon*, the biggest of all. I remember how proud I was when we first bred this gorgeous grey-blue bird at Belle Vue Zoo, Manchester, in the early 1970s.

As a family, pigeons have been very successful and have been involved with human beings for thousands of years. White doves were held sacred in many ancient religions. To the Romans they were love-birds, the special birds of Venus, the goddess of love. The ancient Israelites saw them as symbols of purity, and they remind Christians of the Holy Spirit (the Bible says that, when Jesus was baptized, the Holy Spirit came down on him 'like a dove'). Muslims will not kill doves if they can help it. On the other hand, some superstitions hold that doves are unlucky. Welsh miners used to think that if they saw one flying around a pithead there would be a

The collared dove

disaster in the pit.

Pigeons have done their bit in wartime. When Paris was under siege in 1870 during the Franco-Prussian War, carrier pigeons were used to take messages out of the city. These messages took the form of letters reduced in size by special photography so that one pigeon could carry lots of letters at the same time. In the First World War one bird carried important messages through the middle of a raging battle and was awarded a medal! In the Second World War the RAF dropped boxes of carrier pigeons behind enemy lines by parachute, so that they could be used to send messages back to London.

Town pigeons, like the rest of their family, have plump stocky bodies with a small head and bill and short legs. They eat a wide variety of foods and unlike most birds drink by sucking water without raising their heads. Other birds dip their beaks into the water, scoop up a few drops and then throw back their heads to swallow.

Pigeons are very good at flying and can travel thousands of miles. The fastest racing pigeon could fly at a speed of 70 km per hour. Like starlings, pigeons can find their way by the sun and stars and have an in-built magnetic compass. We also know that they must be able to see the horizon when flying in order to find their way home.

The town pigeon has some interesting relatives

Unlike all other birds except flamingoes and the *male* emperor penguin, pigeons produce *milk* for their young. This milk is produced not in an udder (as in cows and other mammals) but inside the crop, a sort of stomach at the bottom of the throat. The milk is rather thick and contains lots of protein, fats, minerals and vitamins. It is brought up from the crop and the young birds put their bills into the adults' mouth to drink it. Both males and females produce milk.

Like their wild cousins, town pigeons feed on the ground. In winter they depend on the scraps dropped or thrown away by man, or the bits of bread and other food thrown down to them by friendly people. In summer and autumn they also eat seeds. When disturbed, they fly away clapping their wings together. This is probably a warning-signal to other pigeons.

Males and females are difficult to tell apart except in the mating-season, when the males put on an amusing but beautiful display of strutting, bowing and puffing out their chests to attract the females. Often pigeons nest together in small colonies. Loose nests of twigs and dried grass or paper are built under eaves or on the sheltered ledges of buildings. 2–4 clutches of 2 white eggs are laid between March and September. Both parents incubate the eggs, and the young birds are ready to fly at about 5 weeks of age.

Many town pigeons that you will see are not in the best of health. Some of them limp quite badly. They often have damaged legs and diseased joints, and they may have wire or bits of thread caught round their toes or legs. They pick up infectious diseases, including food-poisoning bacteria, and can spread illnesses such as tuberculosis to other birds in farms or zoos when flying over or going in search of food. Nevertheless I must admit that I am still quite fond of these interesting birds, and love to sneak them a crumb or two even when there are notices telling me I mustn't.

The pigeon chick gets milk from its parent's mouth.

Pigeons make loose, untidy nests

The Feral Cat

Do you suffer from ailurophilia? If so, you're in good company. Kings, popes, presidents and prime ministers have had it, and I certainly have it too! No, it isn't a disease but the love of cats. And of course the town is full of cats, cats who are owned by people. Or perhaps I shouldn't say 'owned'. Cats, unlike dogs, are too independent to be owned. Many cats own people. They please themselves what they do, and expect to have their own way.

The feral cat, almost wild

But there is another kind of cat that shares towns with people. This is the *feral cat*, the cat you see alone or in groups in the old railway yard or graveyard, on waste ground or in Fitzroy Square in London. Although some of these creatures may be just stray domestic cats, animals out on the prowl or abandoned by their owners, there is a population of cats that are descended from the tame domestic puss but are returning to being true wild cats. They are far more like real wild cats than the contented Siamese or Persian curled up in front of the fire is. You may not realize it as a battered-looking tom cat slips quietly away from you over a coal-tip, but there goes one of nature's deadliest hunters. Under the skin he is basically the same creature as the tiger, the lion and the leopard, as you will see if you can watch him more closely (not an easy thing to do).

The domestic cat in Europe and America probably started off as a cross between two wild species, *Felis sylvestris* and *Felis lybica*. We can be fairly certain that the first tame cats were tabbies and looked very similar to the true *wild cat*, a species that still manages to survive in lonely Scottish forests.

Feral cats are social animals and like being in groups. Lions are like this, but most other truly wild cats live and hunt alone. Also, most species of wild cat cannot breed with other species, but feral cats do sometimes cross with African and European wild cats and their kittens may be either wild or tame

Feral cats are built just like a leopard, lean and muscular. They stay in trim without having to do any specia exercises, though like other cats they like to have a good stretch and this ma help them to keep their bodies ready to fight. The cat has a most elastic body. The backbone is held together by muscles, and this means that the spine can bend and turn much more easily than a human's can. The shoulder join is designed so that the fore-legs can be turned in almost any direction. All thi makes the cat very quick and very nimble, able to spring and pounce and twist and run with incredible ease.

The kitten has 24 teeth. These are replaced by 30 adult teeth, 16 in the upper jaw and 14 in the lower. All cat tend to bite their prey in the neck, killing it by breaking its neck. It is fascinating to note that the distance between the left and right fang teeth f

Tiger and cat: basically the same

a cat is the same as the width of the neck-joint of its usual prey. A feral or domestic cat has its fang teeth the right distance apart to break the neck of a mouse, and the tiger's are designed to kill the deer and wild pig. There are special nerves linked to the fang teeth of the cat. These sense in the twinkling of an eye when the points of the teeth are in exactly the right place over the neck-joints of the prey. When the nerves tell the brain that the teeth are in the right place, the brain at once tells the jaw muscles to close.

A cat's eyes work well in the dimmest light. At the back of the eye there is a screen made of crystals that reflects every available speck of light and helps the cat to see things we can't. This crystal screen is what makes a cat's eyes flash in the dark.

The cat has wonderful hearing. We have only 6 muscles in our ears, but the cat has 30, which allows it to turn its ears very quickly and accurately to find where a sound is coming from. A cat can turn its ears far more quickly than a dog can. Just watch your own cat's ears when it hears a strange noise under the table!

Cats also have a wonderful sense of smell. Their noses are particularly sensitive to nitrogen, which is given off when food is starting to go bad. This

The feral cat walks his patch

The cat has teeth the right distance apart to break the mouse's neck

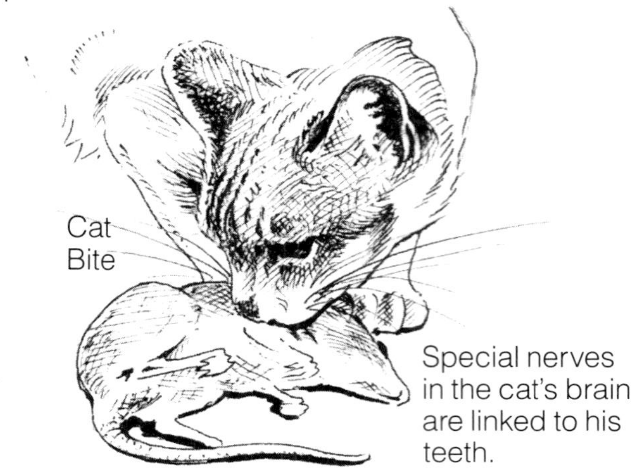

The amazing bite of the cat

explains why a cat refuses to eat anything that is slightly 'off'.

We do not fully understand how a cat uses its whiskers, but we know that they have something to do with touch. Removing them can upset a cat for some time. We also know that in the dark a cat's whiskers are amazingly sensitive, helping it to identify things it cannot see.

A ginger Tom at home with friend

A cat has special muscles that allow it to draw in its claws and also to spread them out – for instance, to obtain a better grip. Dogs do not have these muscles, so their claws are always fixed in the same position.

Cats can run at speeds of up to 27 miles per hour, compared with 45 miles per hour for a greyhound and 63 miles per hour for a cheetah. When cats are walking, the front and back legs on the same side move in the same way at the same time. So, for instance, if the front left leg moves forward, the back left leg does too. The only other animals that do this are the camel and the giraffe.

Thanks to their elastic bodies and the extra-fast nerve-link between their ears, brain and muscles, cats can land with their feet down even when falling only a short way. They have also been known to survive very long falls – even from the nineteenth floor of a very tall building (about 60 m). It is extremely cruel, though, to test how far a cat can fall without hurting itself.

Feral cats live in groups. The roughest, toughest tom is 'top cat', and the other cats look up to him as the

boss. Every cat knows its place in the group. All cats are territorial, with their own hunting-grounds. Although female feral cats have fairly small territories, they will fight harder to keep them than a tom who controls a large area. The cats mark out their territory by scratching trees, posts and fences, and by spraying urine or rubbing things with a substance secreted by glands on the head and face. Some toms in an area with few cats may control 20 or more hectares. Within its property each cat has its favourite place for sleeping, watching and sunbathing.

Beyond the private territories lie hunting- and meeting-grounds belonging to the whole group. To reach these places cats have a system of pathways that run along the edge of other cats' private territories and areas without cats. Some pathways are the private property of one cat, but most of these paths are 'main roads' that can be used by all. However, there is a 'highway code' for cats using these paths. Any cat approaching a main path from another track must give way to a cat that is

The territories of a cat society

already on the main path.

Cats' meeting-grounds are like clubs where the cats meet at night, groom each other's coats and generally enjoy each other's company. Cats communicate with one another in a variety of ways, including smell, sound and 'body language'. They can produce at least 16 different sounds, and they can signal to each other by the way they move, hold their tails, turn their faces, and so on.

The life of feral cats is often a hard one. People tend to treat feral cats as pests, and sometimes try to poison them, though it is against the law to do this in England. Disease is also common among these cats. Where there are too many cats, attempts have been made to control their numbers by putting out food containing drugs that stop females from having kittens. This at least makes it easier for the other cats to find enough food.

The Bluebottle

When summer comes to town, you are sure to hear the buzz of the bluebottle's wings and the 'plop' as it crashes into a window. People do not like bluebottles in their houses, and no wonder! They are often found in the most unpleasant places and can carry all sorts of diseases. In fact, they are not much better than the house-fly, which can spread over 60 important diseases to people and animals – more than any other creature in the world. The name 'bluebottle' has got nothing to do with bottles, but comes from a Gaelic word (*boiteag*) meaning a maggot. On the other hand, bluebottles really are blue. Another name for them is 'blow-flies'. They are fat and gleaming and come into the house in search of food.

The bluebottle is one of 50,000 different species that belong to the family of 2-winged flies called *Diptera*, which feed on liquids. Like all insects they have a body divided into 3 parts (head, thorax or chest and abdomen) and 6 legs. They possess large compound eyes that can see all around them and antennae that are extremely sensitive to smells. They feed by sucking through a sort of tube called a 'proboscis', which is operated by a pump in the head. As soon as the proboscis touches food (sugar, for example), it will start sucking, and will carry on doing this for a while even if the head is cut off from the body! The proboscis contains a set of very tiny teeth which it uses to grate the surface of substances such as sugar so that it can suck them up. (It grates and sucks the food at the same time.) The broad 'lips' at the tip of the proboscis are fringed with hairs that give the fly a sense of taste. The body-surface and legs of the bluebottle are covered in fine hairs which help the antennae pick up the smell of nitrogen in the air. This attracts the insect to dung, meat or dead animals over distances of several

A bluebottle: unpopular insect

kilometres. The antennae are also very sensitive to sounds (only a little less sensitive than the human ear) and help the bluebottle tell which way the wind is blowing, and how strong it is. By this means it can control its speed and flight-path.

The movement of the wings is produced by two groups of very elastic muscles attached to the thorax. When one group of muscles pulls the wing up, the other group is stretched, and the same happens to the sides of the thorax. At a certain point the 'elastic' clicks back and the first group of muscles is stretched while the other group pulls the wings down. This is repeated over and over again. The buzzing noise of the insect's flight comes from the vibration of the thorax as it is tugged to and fro by the flight muscles. The rubbing at the bases of the wings may also have something to do with it.

Bluebottles feed mainly on dung and dead flesh, sucking the juices from them and spreading the germs they pick up through doing this. They lay small clusters of long white eggs on the meat. These eggs are tiny but can be seen quite easily. Depending how warm and damp it is, the eggs hatch in 12–72 hours and produce tiny larvae or maggots with waxy skins. The maggots' mouth-parts and the casing round the throat are dark and horny and can be seen through the head, which is clear. Inside the throat-casing are tiny cells sensitive

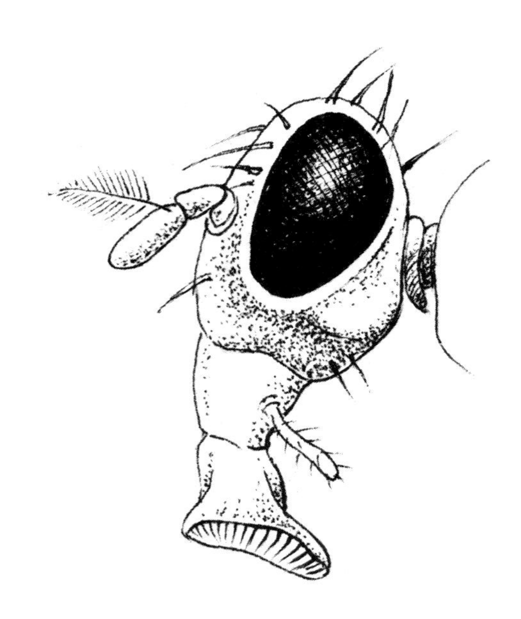

The proboscis is made for sucking liquid

White eggs shaped like tombstones

to light. If there is any light around, they react and tell the maggot to burrow into the meat instead of staying at the surface, where it would dry up and die.

British bluebottle maggots only attack dead flesh, and if they are clean they are not harmful and can even be useful. During the First World War they were bred for use in hospitals to clean up the wounds of soldiers with gangrene by eating the dead flesh. But some British greenbottles (flies similar to bluebottles) and some foreign bluebottles produce maggots that will attack living flesh. Such species often lay their eggs on sheep and the maggots make nasty open sores beneath the fleece that sometimes cause the death of the poor beast. This problem, commonly called 'fly-strike' by shepherds, can sometimes be very serious in Australia, South Africa and Britain. Other animals may be attacked in this way too.

After 2–21 days, depending on where they are, the maggots turn into pupae. Their outer skin hardens into a case and turns dark brown. Usually the pupae drop off the meat or body. In the olden days, every monastery had its carp pond – the monks enjoyed the delicious fish for meals on Fridays, the traditional day for eating fish. They would hang some dead rabbits over the pond, and bluebottle maggots would soon be feeding on the bodies. When the maggots turned into pupae and dropped off the meat, the fish were swimming below, ready to gobble them up. It was a sort of mediaeval automatic fish-feeding device!

Maggots and pupae of a bluebottle

Maggots are much used by fishermen as fish-bait. There are even maggot-farms where millions of maggots are bred each week from specially chosen bluebottles and feed on tons of waste fish. Such farms are very smelly and are usually right out in the country. Fishermen can buy live maggots that have been coloured with non-poisonous dyes. Every fisherman has his own idea of which colour is likely to appeal most to a particular kind of fish on a particular day.

The mediaeval monks' automatic carp-feeding device

After a period that may be as short as 3 days, though it is much longer in winter, the adult fly cracks its way out of the pupal case by puffing up a special bladder with blood. The new bluebottle is at first soft and flimsy with limp wings, but it immediately swallows air and puffs itself up inside to over twice the size. This pressure forces blood into the wings and stretches them. 20–30 minutes after emerging, the wings are ready to use, and within 1–2 hours the body-casing of the bluebottle has hardened and darkened.

It is a very good thing that flies that breed so quickly have so many enemies. Many other insects eat them, and so do a whole range of other creatures, including bats, cats and many smaller mammals. All these help to keep under control a creature that is a great pest, and one of the most unwelcome members of the zoo in the town.

Attracted by smell received via their antennae, flies find meat with great ease

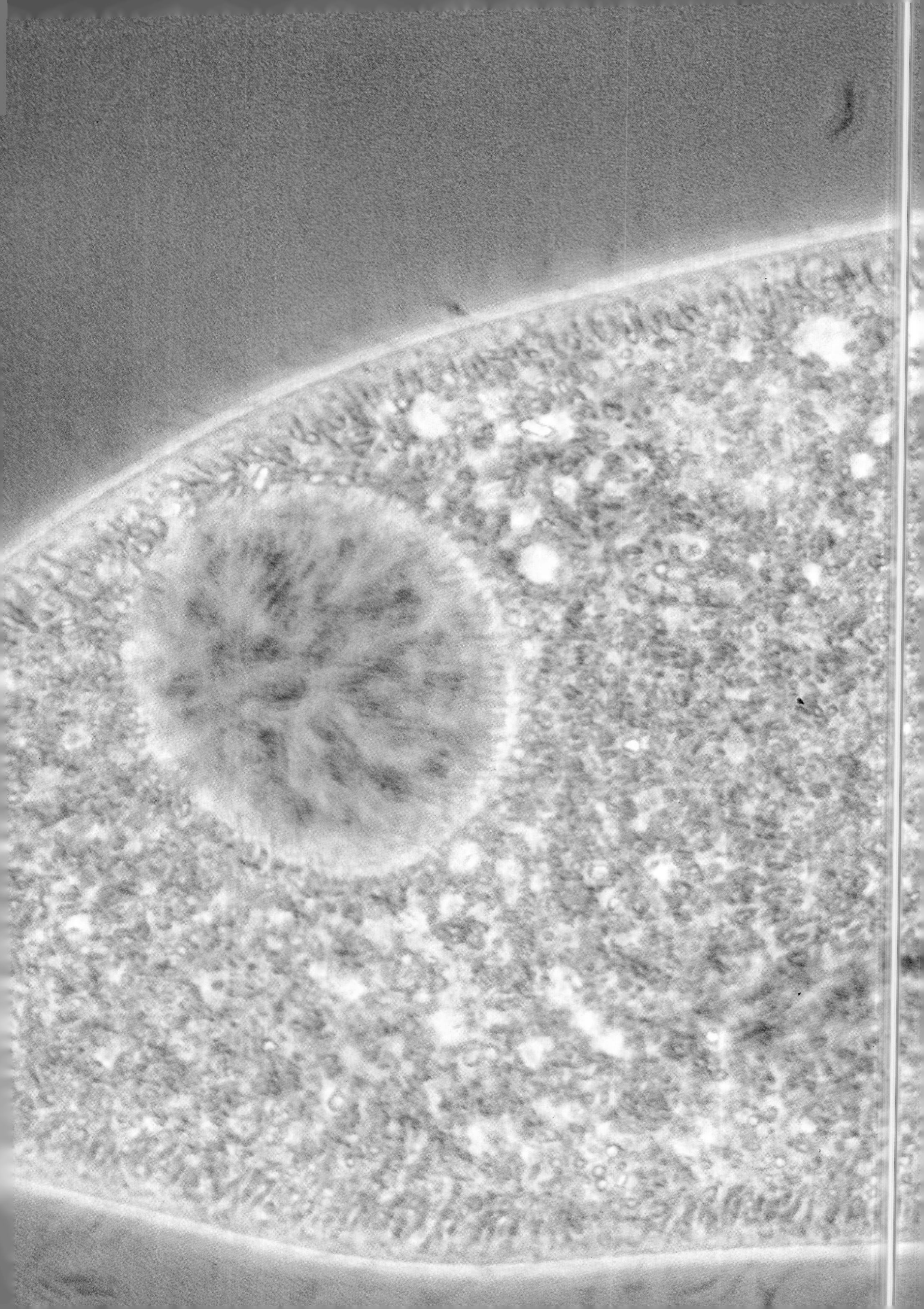

The
ZOO
in you
Discover the animals which
live in you

Bacteria

The world is literally teeming with germs, which we call microbes. One form of microbe is the *bacterium*, which many scientists consider to be a lowly form of plant. Bacteria are living creatures composed of a single cell. A human being is made up of many millions of cells, so it is not surprising that you cannot see a bacterium without the aid of a powerful microscope. Bacteria are measured in microns (1 micron is 1 millionth of a metre), and they can be found everywhere, from the bottom of the ocean to the top of mountains, in the air, in the soil, and inside plants and animals.

Many bacteria are harmless, friendly and very useful. Life on earth would be impossible without them. They are tiny chemical wizards, organizing all sorts of chemical reactions. They help you digest your food so that your body can use it. They help make it possible for milk to become butter, cheese and yogurt, for grape-juice to turn into wine, and so on. They break down and build up millions of different substances. They create nitrogen in the soil, making it fertile so that it grows the plants on which you and all living creatures depend. You carry thousands of millions of them on and within your body. To them you are their world. To you they are part of your personal zoo, and most of the time, I hope, you should get on well together. But sometimes things go wrong or unfriendly bacteria enter the body, and this is when you fall ill.

Bacteria under the microscope

Bacteria may be plants, but they aren't green as they contain no chlorophyll, which is what plants need to obtain food from the air. It may be that bacteria are closely related to those other non-green plants the *fungi*. They come in a variety of shapes but there are three main designs: round ones called *cocci*, rod-shaped ones called

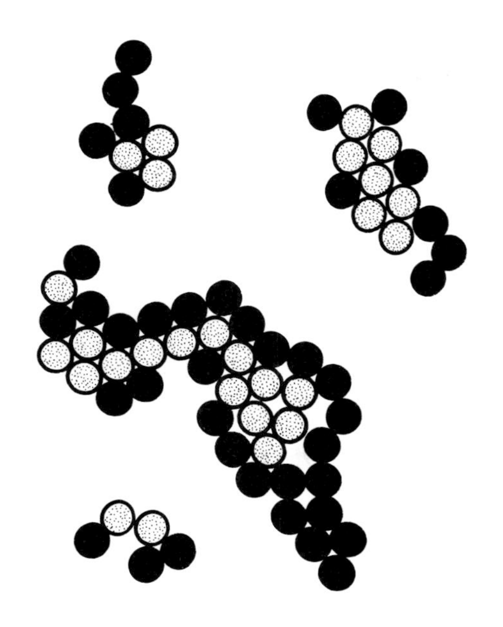

Coccus bacteria

bacilli and spirally twisted ones called *spirilla*. As I have said, some cause illnesses. *Staphylococci* are cocci that cause 'boils' in human skin. One form of bacillus causes tuberculosis, a disease of the lungs, and one type of spirillum causes a kidney disease of dogs.

Bacteria multiply by dividing into two without any need for mating, as there are no males and females. The rate at which bacteria multiply is very fast and becomes faster the warmer it gets. If it takes 30 minutes for a bacterium of a certain species to divide into two, and that rate is kept up, one such bacterium will multiply into 1000 million bacteria within 15 hours! (But remember how small they are: a single teaspoon could hold 160,000 million bacteria of average size.) Why, then, don't bacteria swamp the world? First, there isn't enough food around for them to keep multiplying at the same rate all the time. Secondly, as they increase in numbers their waste-products (particularly acids) increase, and this slows down the speed at which they can multiply.

In order to live, bacteria need moisture, warmth and food. Their surroundings must contain at least 4 per cent water, while the minimum

Spirillum bacteria

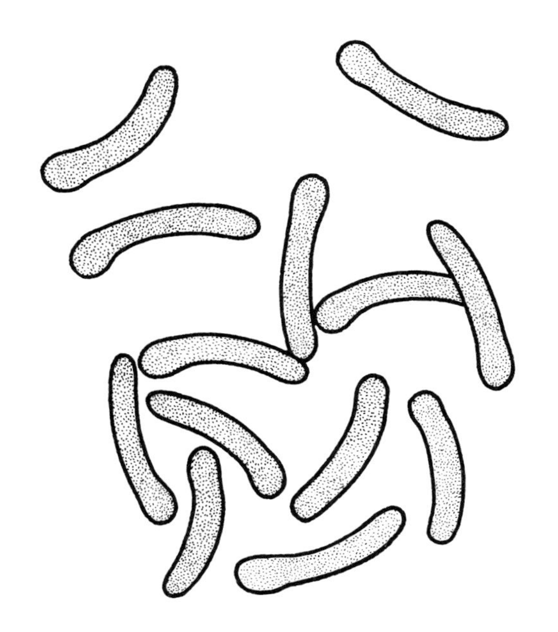

Bacillus bacteria

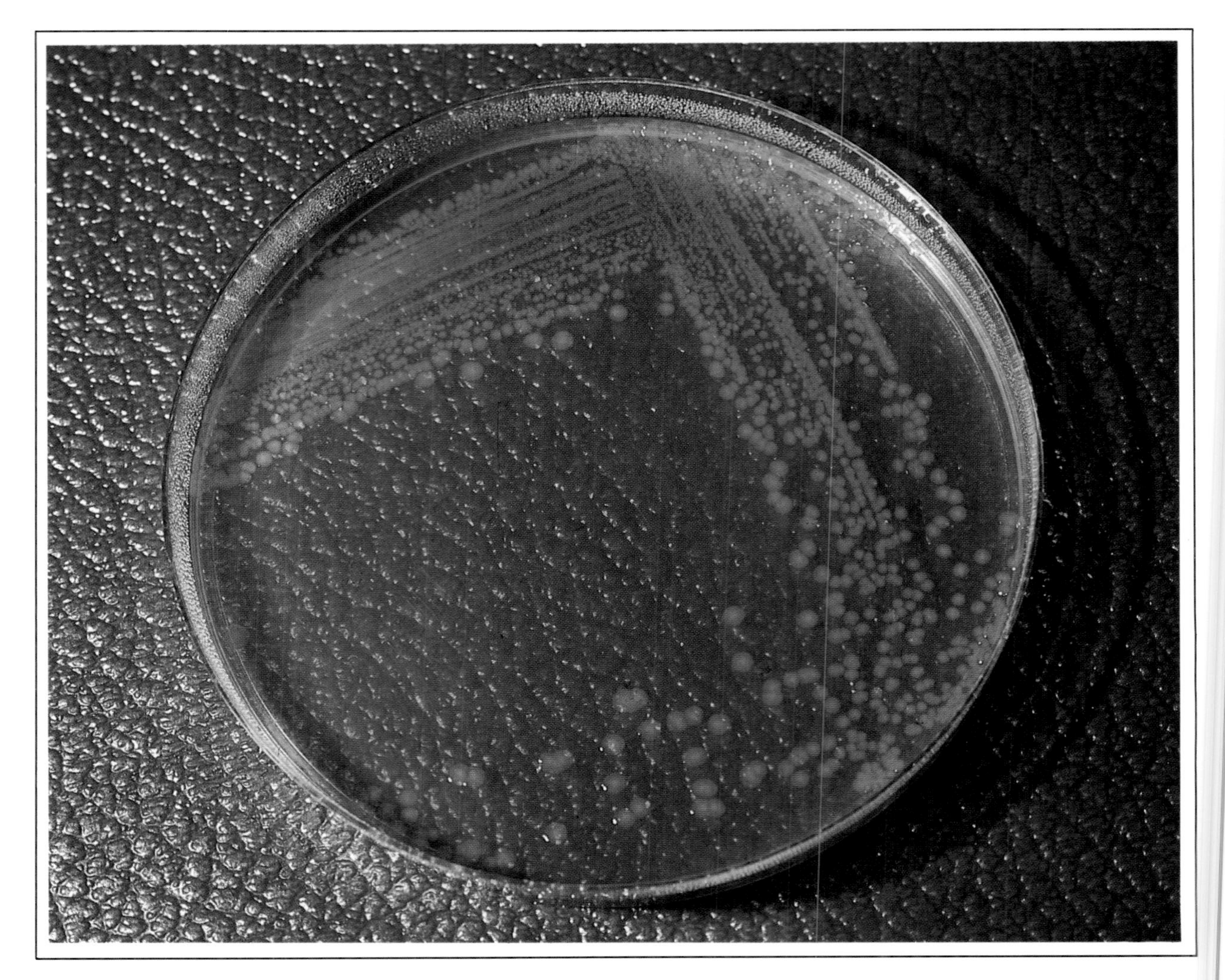

Bacteria growing on a jelly plate

temperature they require depends on the species. Some bacteria can obtain chemicals from the air and most need a source of nitrogen, together with tiny quantities of other chemical elements that are readily available throughout nature. Although some bacteria need oxygen, others can survive *without* it. Most bacteria prefer darkness to light, and direct sunlight kills most species.

At least 80 different kinds of bacteria live harmlessly in your mouth, and the total that leave your body every day when you go to the toilet ranges from an amazing 100 thousand millions to an even more staggering 100 million millions! The bacteria that make you their home are to be found on nearly every surface of the body that is open to the air or that can be reached from the outside through passages in your body. Many of these bacteria are not parasites, which have to live on you to be able to survive, but are simply lodgers taking advantage of the darkness, warmth, moisture and plentiful food that they find there. Other bacteria living on man are true parasites, unable to live anywhere else in nature. They have a special relationship with the surfaces of our bodies and, when things go wrong, can go through the surfaces into other parts of the body, where they are attacked and destroyed by the amazing array of defence systems built into the body. If they can overcome these defences for a while, they cause illness. Don't forget *all* healthy animals and plants have bacteria growing on their surfaces.

The body's defences against invasion by germs are many and varied. The strong acid of the stomach juices and the tears of the eyes contain chemicals that kill germs. Coughing helps to protect the breathing system from bacteria in the air, and so do the small hairs in the nose and the fine hairs on the bronchial (breathing) tubes of the lungs. Any unwanted bacteria that get inside the body are detected at once by the body tissues (the layers of cells that make up the various parts of your body), which send special sentry cells to the spot to fight and gobble up the germs. The body also uses special chemicals called 'antibodies' that are found in the blood and other body fluids. These have the power to lock onto and destroy invaders.

Large numbers of bacteria occur naturally on your skin. There are more in some places than in others. The hairless parts of the face and hands do not have very many, but sweaty and oily places such as the corners of the nose and the spaces between the toes have a lot. The navel or 'belly button' isn't overcrowded, but there are plenty of bacteria in the opening to the ear. The biggest numbers are found in the groin (where your legs join) and the armpits.

The bladder and the urethra (the place where urine is stored and the tube through which is passes out of your body) are usually sterile, which means free of bacteria. Urine becomes contaminated with bacteria only after leaving the body, as do sweat and saliva once they have left the glands that produce them. Saliva picks up bacteria in the mouth, and in a healthy person one spit contains 100–1000 million bacteria per cubic centimetre. Most clean skin contains around 5 million bacteria per square centimetre, which makes a total of 100,000 million germs on the skin of one adult!

Only when the resistance of the body to disease breaks down can some of the germs that normally live on your skin and any others that happen to land on you manage to break through the defences. These defences can be weakened if you are too cold, if you are not eating the right food and don't have all the vitamins you need, if you are already ill or have cut yourself badly. If you need extra help to fight off bacteria, the doctor may decide to use antibiotics, chemicals mostly developed from germ-killers found naturally in certain species of fungi.

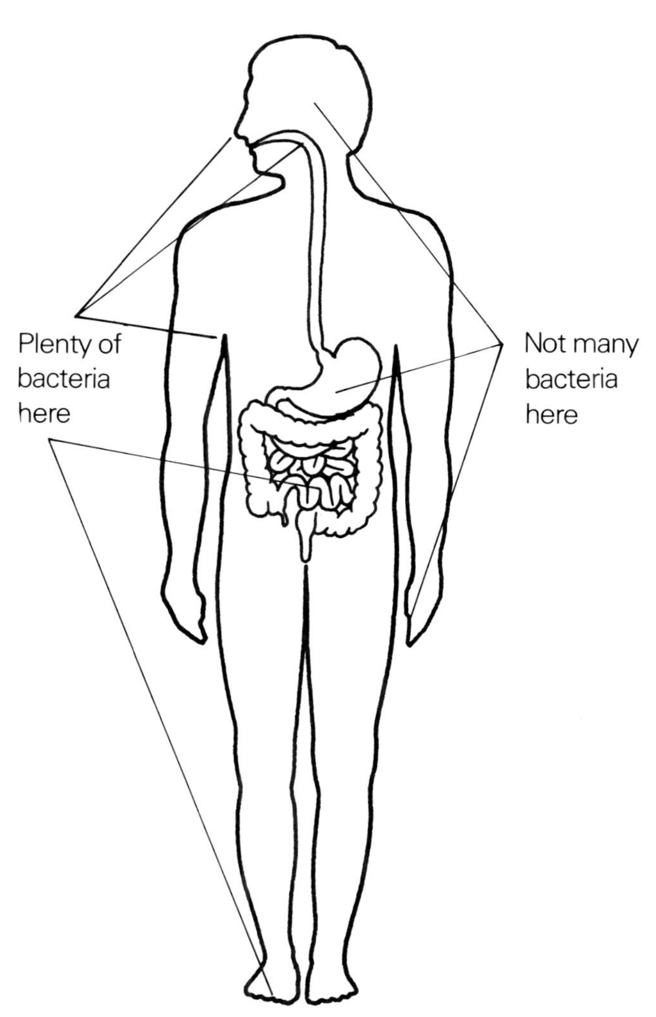

Some parts of your body are home to more bacteria than others

The Virus

In the zoo in you, the smallest inhabitants, far tinier than bacteria, are a strange and important group of creatures called viruses. These are so small that they are measured in nanometres (1 nanometre is 1 thousand millionth of a metre or 1 thousandth of a micron). The trouble is, we are not absolutely sure whether these things are dead or alive! (You'll see what I mean in a moment.)

Viruses can only grow in an animal or plant cell and have bodies composed of a core of acid covered by a coat of protein and sometimes some fatty and starchy material. They are so very tiny that you cannot see them with your student microscope, and no other microscope that uses light is any use either. They can only be seen with an electron microscope.

Viruses come in a variety of shapes: some are round, some are shaped like loaves, some have rod-like bodies, and some are hexagonal (with six sides). In some ways they behave like non-living objects: for example, they can be turned into crystals, in the same way as non-living things such as sugar or salt can. In other ways they are like living organisms: for example, they can multiply themselves. To do this they first attach themselves to, and then enter, a living animal or plant cell. Once inside they multiply by using the chemicals already in the cell to make more viruses like themselves. This means that viruses can only be grown in laboratories if they are provided with living cells that they can enter. These

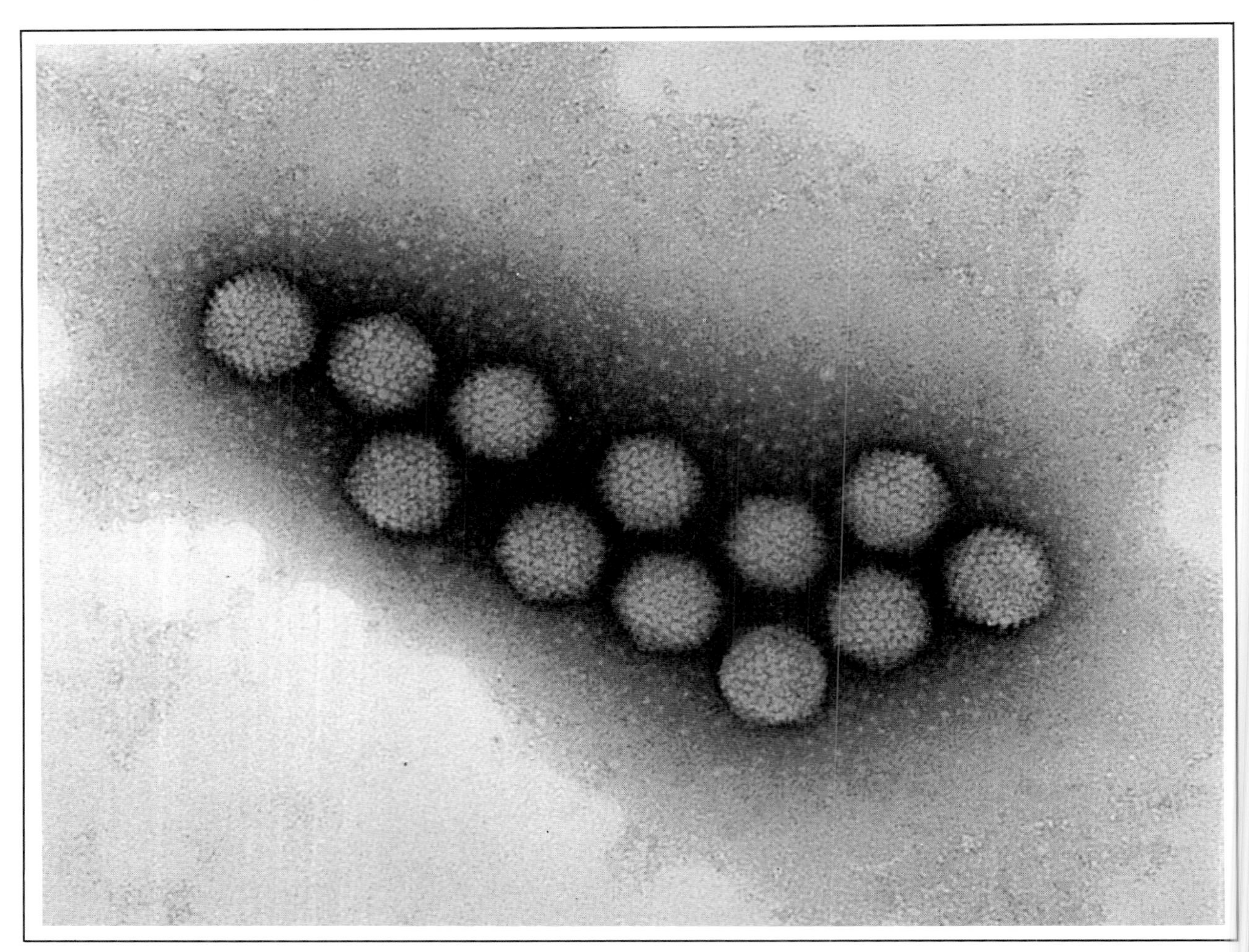

Adeno-viruses magnified 120,000 times

cells can be either those of living animals or plants, or those of what are called 'tissue cultures'. Tissue cultures are colonies of living cells that are kept alive in special 'soups' of nourishing liquids.

Sometimes viruses can live inside a cell without causing any trouble. They appear to be inactive or 'dormant'. 'Cold-sore' viruses may remain dormant for months or years in this way within the cells of your lips. They are 'woken up' when the cell's resistance to attack is weakened. This may happen when you catch a cold or suffer from other illness, or when the cell is affected by something such as bright sunlight. (Cold sores tend to flare up when people who carry the virus go on holiday to a hot country or spend a lot of time in the sun.) When the virus has been woken up, it begins to multiply and damages or kills the cell. In the case of the cold-sore virus, the cell-damage results in tingly little blisters in the skin.

The body has a number of good defences against virus attack. These include the production of antibodies, which, as we saw when looking at bacteria, are chemicals that circulate in the blood and other body fluids and attach themselves to invaders and destroy them. They can do this also with viruses. Also, cells infected with viruses make a special substance called 'interferon', which can spread to healthy cells and protect them by 'interfering' with a virus's ability to

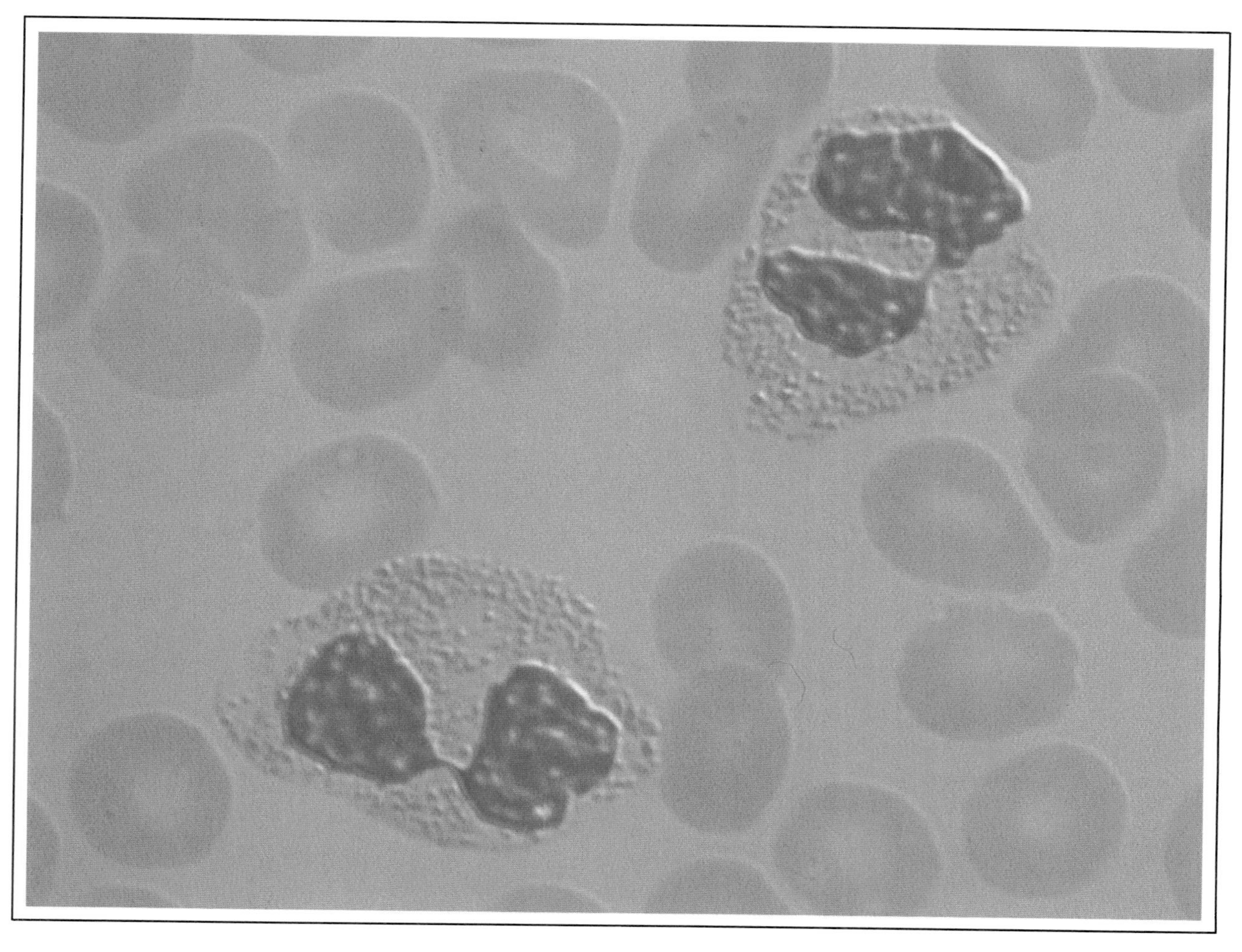

Blood magnified. The two white cells in the picture attack bacteria but are no defence against viruses

enter a cell and multiply. Viruses cannot be attacked by antibiotics, which are used to fight bacteria, but are often used when people or animals have virus diseases so that bacteria can't take the chance to make things worse. In this way, the body is protected from further infections and can concentrate on getting rid of the viruses.

Like bacteria, viruses can be turned into vaccines, which are usually fed into the body by injections and help protect humans and animals against disease. A vaccine for viral infections is made either by using a dead virus or, more often, by using one that has been weakened in the laboratory so that it cannot cause disease even though it is still alive. When given to the patient, the vaccine does not produce illness but *does* stimulate the body to produce defensive antibodies. These antibodies circulate in the body for a long time after vaccination and, even when their level in the blood falls, the body cells remember how to make them should viruses that haven't been weakened ever attack the body.

Your pet animals also can fall ill from diseases caused by viruses. There are viruses that are specially likely to attack them. Dogs can be attacked by viruses that cause liver disease or distemper, for example. Cats can suffer from viruses that attack the liver, cause diarrhoea or produce cat influenza (the sort of 'flu' that affects cats). It is wise to have puppies and kittens vaccinated against these viruses just as human babies are vaccinated against the virus that causes poliomyelitis or 'polio' – a killer disease that thanks to vaccination is now very rare. As a vet, I often see and treat viral diseases in all sorts of animals, ranging from dolphins to gorillas and elephants to falcons. Sealions are particularly at risk from a virus that causes a skin disease rather like chicken-pox, which is also caused by a virus. I have seen orang-outang babies with measles caused by the same virus as infects children with this disease.

Reptiles, amphibians, fish, insects and even bacteria can all be infected by certain kinds of virus. Plants have a wide range of their own viruses, many of which cause them to become deformed. There are for example viral diseases of the tobacco plant and the potato. One of the worst viral diseases that can attack man is rabies. This horrible disease is usually caused by being bitten by a mad dog, but, thanks to very strict laws about taking

Some viruses and things they can cause

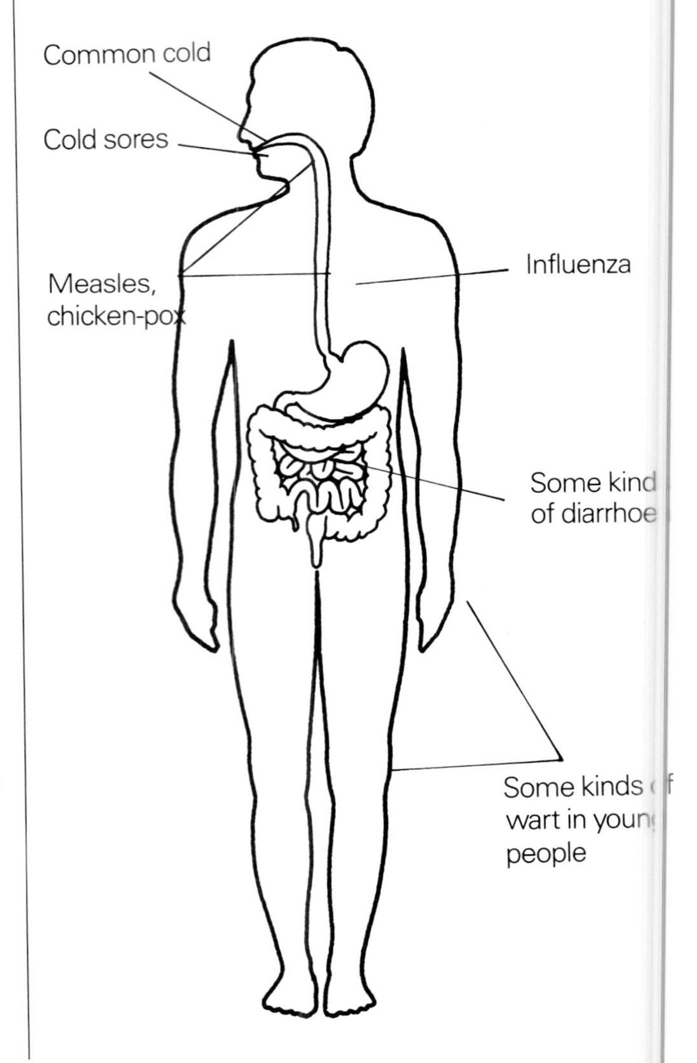

animals from one country to another, it hardly ever occurs in Britain. Other bad viral diseases include the tropical disease yellow fever, and smallpox, which used to be common in Europe and America but has now just about died out because of the use of vaccines. If you are travelling to a country where some of the worst viral diseases are still found, you will have to be vaccinated against them before you go.

Where did viruses come from? Some scientists have suggested that they arrived here on earth from outer space in showers of dust from comet-tails and small meteors. A much more common idea is that they developed from the cores of plant or animal cells themselves. A third possibility is that they are remnants of more complicated parasites that got into the habit of living inside cells and eventually lost more and more bits of their original bodies as they came to rely more and more on the host cell.

Orang-outangs can catch measles

The Fungus

Some fungi are able to make their home on or in the human (or animal) body. Fungi are a large group of plants which include some of the most primitive forms of plant life known to science. Unlike most plants, they contain no chlorophyll, the green chemical that helps plants to make food

A fungus's body plan

from the gas in the air called carbon dioxide. This process, known as 'photosynthesis', can occur only in daylight. Fungi cannot make their food in this way, so they have to obtain it from dead or decaying animal or plant material or, far less commonly, from living animals or plants. The type that live on dead or decaying cells are called 'saprophytes' while those that depend on living things are 'parasites'.

Fungi are a large family containing hundreds of thousands of species and are very widespread. However, they don't like direct light, or places that are too hot, too cold, too wet or too dry. They grow best in places that are dark, damp and fairly warm.

Fungi are constructed either as microscopic single cells or as branching tubes or filaments known as 'hyphae'. Some of the simplest fungi reproduce from cells called 'spores', which are sometimes clustered together within rounded containers called 'spore-sacs' or 'spore bodies'. The spores split off and start a new plant. More advanced fungi also produce spores, but only do so after male and female cells have joined together.

Although the individual fungus cell is invisible to the naked eye, it can be observed easily using a simple microscope. When large numbers of the cells are present in one place, the crowd can be seen without a microscope, as a white or coloured 'mould'. You have probably seen the moulds that grow on

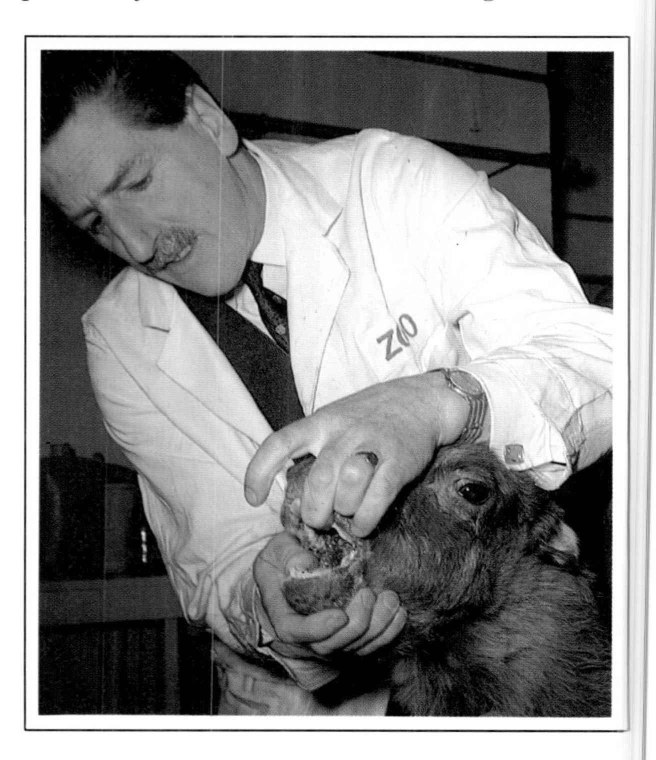

'Thrush' fungus in a baby camel's mouth

stale bread or old jam, and are sure to know the edible mushroom, which is another type of fungus. None of these fungi live in or on human beings. Only a very few species have the knack of surviving among the cells of our bodies,

A toadstool is a fungus

and most of these only do so rarely, even though the spores of fungi are everywhere, blowing about in the air and continually landing on us without our ever seeing them.

Some of the fungi that can live in our bodies usually live in nature as saprophytes, preferring dead or decaying matter. One such is a kind of yeast-type fungus called *Candida* (Latin for 'white'), which causes the condition known as 'thrush' – white spots that often appear in the mouths of babies, particularly when they are being bottle-fed. I've even seen it in baby camels! The spots are actually masses of tiny, branching fungal hyphae. Candida is found naturally in the skin and mouth of human beings, and also in the lining of the alimentary tract (the tube that starts at the mouth and continues with the gullet, stomach and bowels to the opening called the anus, through which the body's waste passes). It can only cause trouble when the body's natural

Saprophytes live on dead stuff

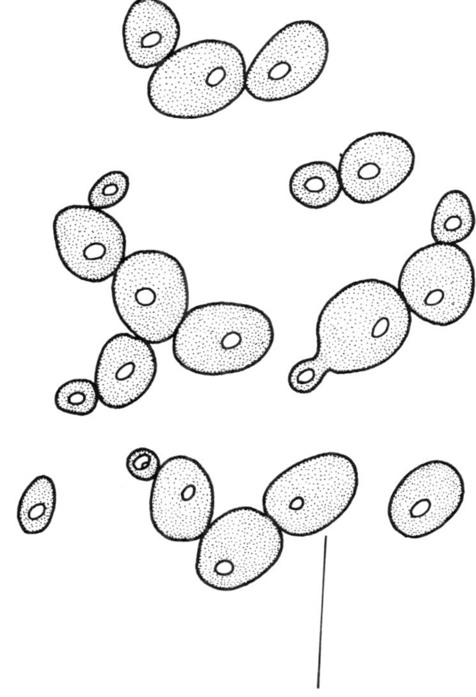

Under a microscope saprophytes look like this

defences are weakened for some reason.

Some fungi live in the human skin if they get the chance. One example is 'ringworm', which has nothing to do with worms but is caused by fungal hyphae that attack the outer layers of skin cells, hair and nails. Some of these fungi are picked up after contact with infected cats, dogs or cattle. Another fairly common fungus ailment is 'athlete's foot'. This again is caused by a species which lives on the skin of the feet, particularly between the toes, and which under normal conditions causes no trouble whatsoever. It only breaks into the skin when conditions are right for it: for example, when the skin is very sweaty or when you don't dry your feet properly with a towel. It is often found in the damp conditions of changing-rooms and swimming-baths and can live for a long time in socks and shoes.

More serious but rare diseases caused by fungi occur in other countries. In South Africa, pot-holers sometimes develop a fungal infection of the lungs after visiting caves where there are large numbers of bats. The fungus lives as a saprophyte on the bats' droppings and the men breathe it in through the air. Another kind of rare fungal disease occurs sometimes in Madagascar, off the coast of Africa. This is a fungus that usually lives as a saprophyte on wooden posts but that under certain conditions can enter a human body and cause lung disease.

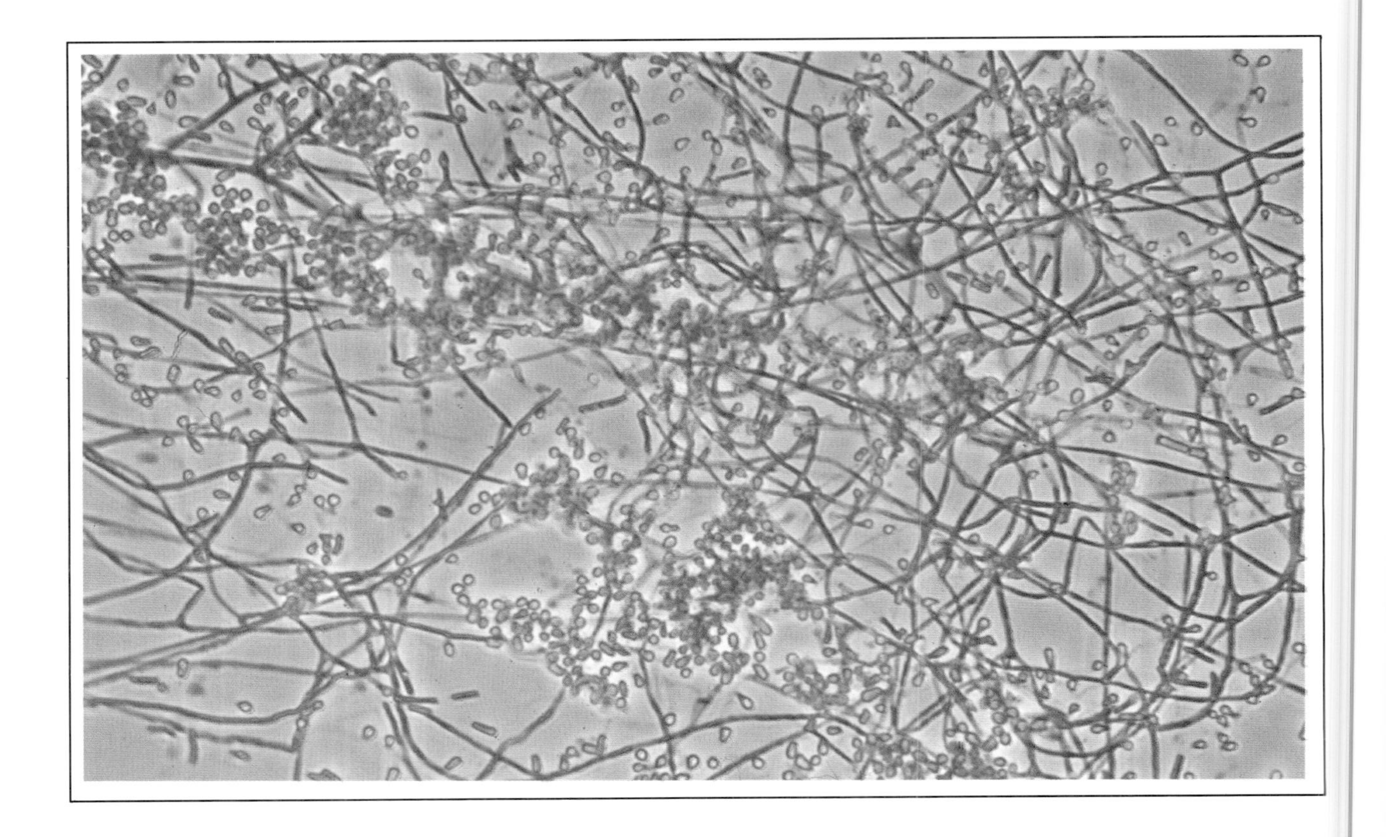

Ringworm fungus in human scalp

The temperature of the human body stops most fungi from establishing a home there. 37°C, the normal temperature of the human body, is too hot for them. Many actually die at a temperature of 40°C. Some fungi, such as the one that can cause ringworm, manage to avoid the high temperature of the inside of the body by only living

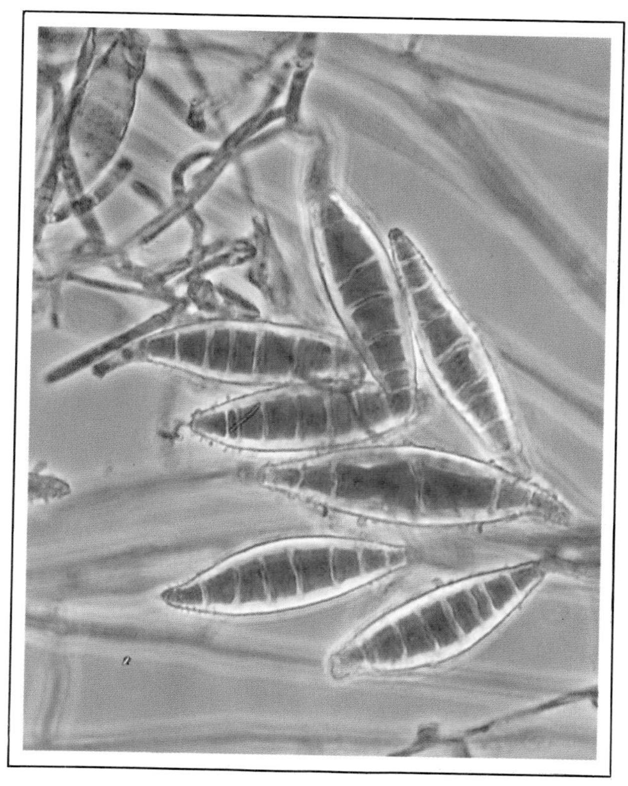

The pretty spores of a fungus causing ringworm in dogs

on the outer layers of the skin and hair, which are cooler. The oil naturally produced by glands in the skin (the sebaceous glands) protects the skin from fungal (and some bacterial) infections. The natural fat is broken down by friendly bacteria living on the skin into fatty acids that make it difficult for fungi to grow. Friendly bacteria help the body to keep down fungal growth in other ways. The bacteria that live in the intestines help to keep in check the fungi that live there by competing with them for living-space and food, and sometimes they actually feed upon them. As on the skin, the bacteria may also produce chemicals such as acids that the fungi do not like.

Antibiotics, the medicines that have proved to be so good at fighting bacteria, do not kill fungi. This means that sometimes, if you take antibiotics for a long time, there are not enough bacteria left to keep down the fungi in the body and they run riot and cause infections. Luckily new medicines that specifically attack fungi have been discovered and are now used by doctors to treat fungal infections when they occur.

One of the most serious fungal illnesses that affects animals is a type of pneumonia (a lung disease) suffered by birds. Young turkeys, penguins and falcons are particularly at risk from it. 'Thrush' may sometimes attack dolphins. Fungi also cause a number of plant diseases, such as potato blight and mildew.

The human body

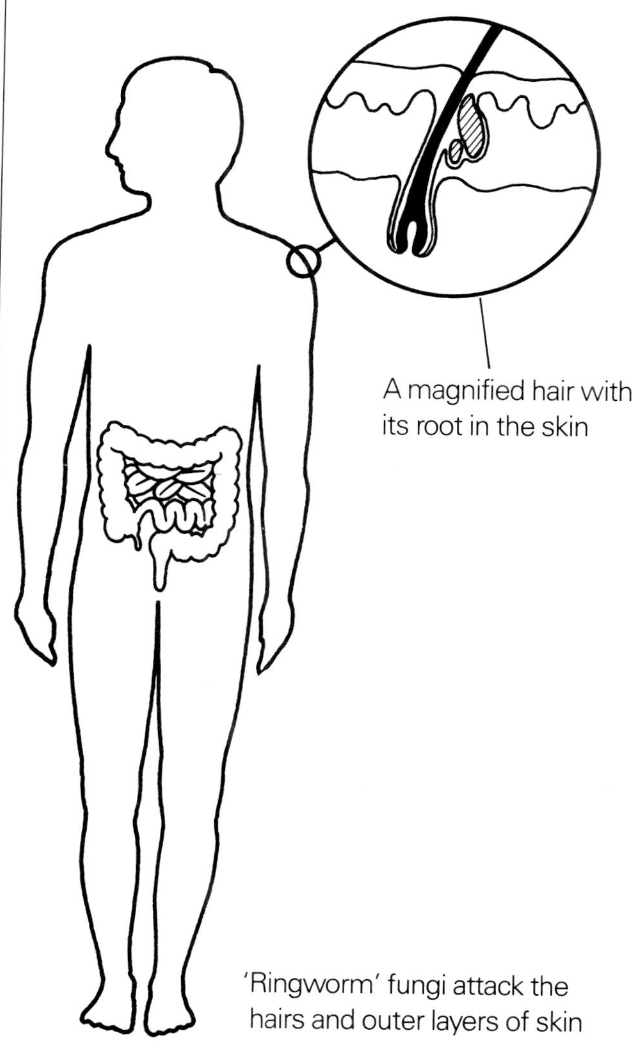

The Amoeba

You will need a microscope to introduce yourselves to the thousands of little lake-dwellers that live happily inside your intestines, paddling about in the dark where there is all the moisture, warmth and food that they could possibly want. These harmless little individuals that spend their lives in the long winding tube from the stomach to the bowels are *protozoa*.

Protozoa are mostly microscopic one-celled creatures that should be classified perhaps half-way between animals and plants. They are found everywhere where there is moisture, in numbers almost as great as those of bacteria. Some species are found throughout the world, while others live only in certain surroundings. Some form part of the plankton (a sort of 'soup' of tiny living things that fish and other creatures feed on) in the oceans. Over 30,000 living species are known to science. They come in an amazing variety of body shapes – from tiny blobs 2 microns long that live within the red blood-cells of animals to the delicate *foraminiferans*, with shells 5 cm across.

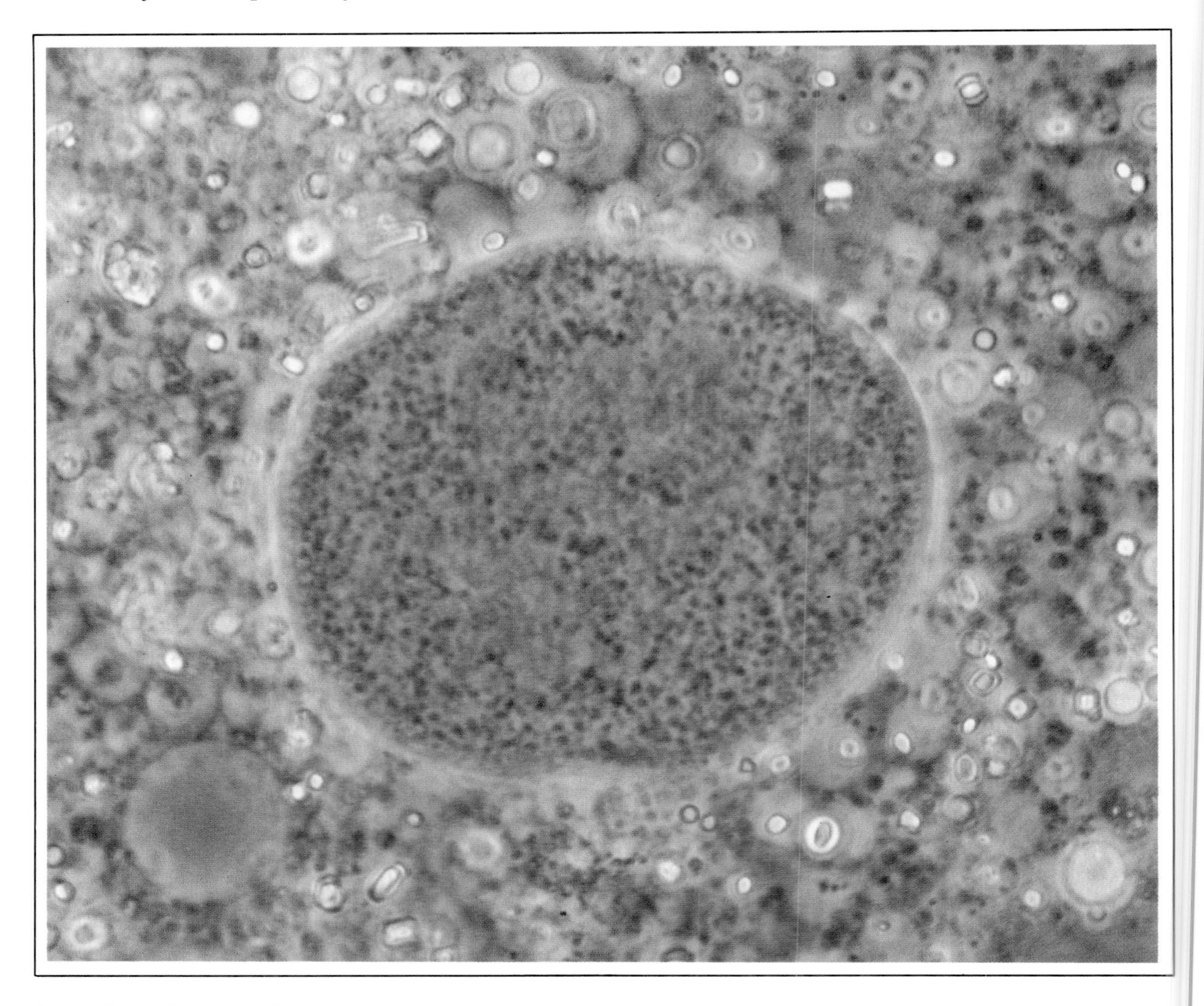

Amoebae highly magnified

Some move by flowing and oozing, others paddle with rows of little 'oars' (cilia) and other wriggle and push themselves along with the aid of a 'tail' (flagellum). Some contain the green

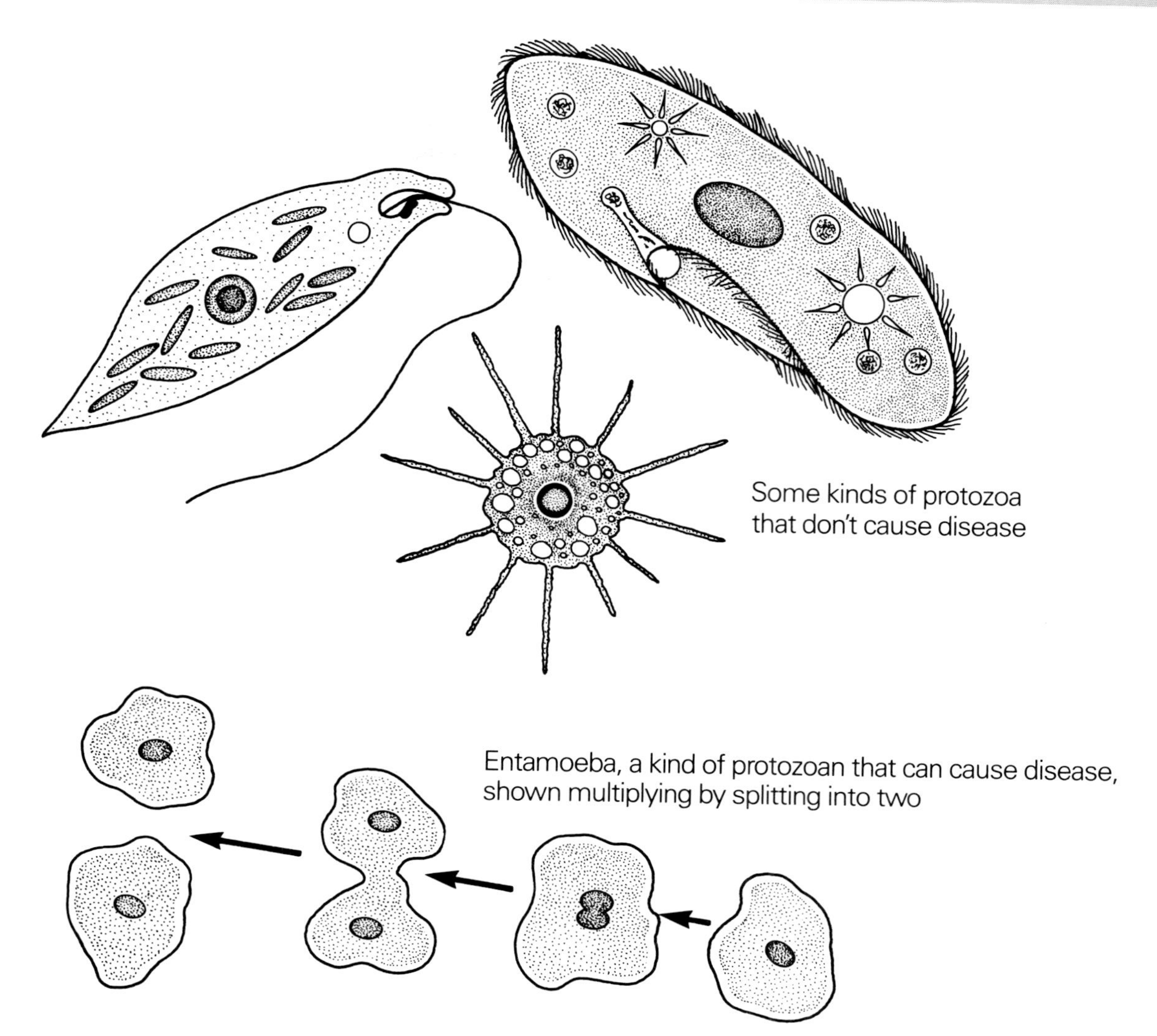

chemical chlorophyll and in daylight can build up starchy foods from simple chemicals around them, and are important links in the food-chain of the ocean. Others live in the soil and feed on bacteria. And, while nearly all the protozoa are 'free-living' (not dependent on other living creatures as parasites) a very few cause disease by living as parasites.

Every biology student is familiar with the free-living *Amoeba proteus*. This tiny protozoan barely visible with the naked eye is found in pond-water. It has no fixed shape, but constantly changes its outline by pushing out parts of its single-cell body. The rest of the body then flows into the spaces left by the parts pushed out and in this way the amoeba moves along. The name given to

the parts pushed out is 'pseudopodia' – Greek for 'false feet', which describes their use very well. The amoeba also uses its pseudopodia to flow round and trap food material in tiny holes which digest the food.

Like bacteria, amoebae multiply by splitting into two. Each of the two parts takes half of the 'nucleus' or core of the old cell. Large numbers of amoebae can be quickly produced by this splitting-process.

Various kinds of amoebae live in the human intestines quite naturally. They live and feed in a very similar way to the *Amoeba proteus* in its pond. Most measure only about 20 microns across. One species that is often present is

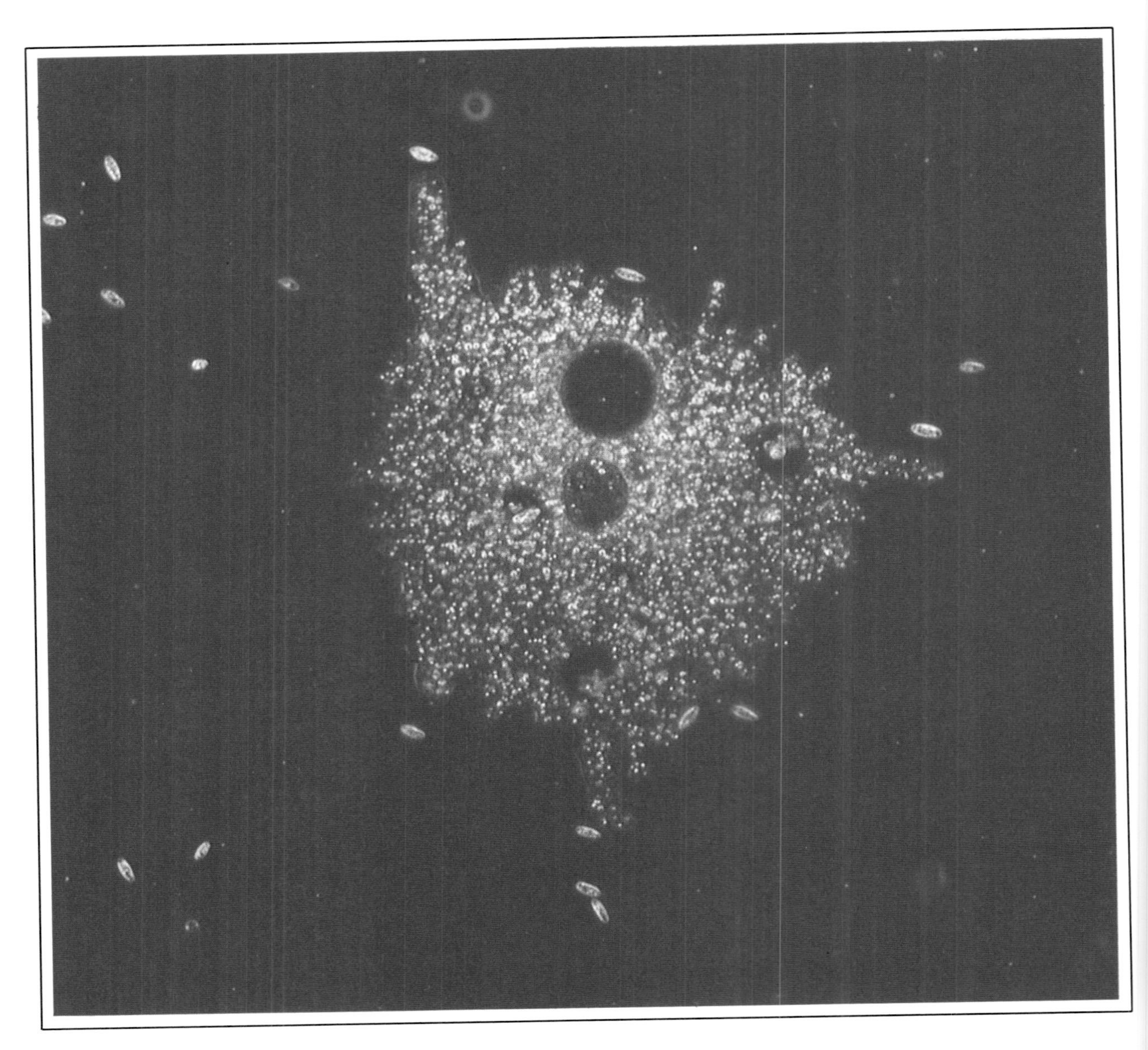

Entamoeba histolytica. Like other amoebae that live in the intestines, it usually feeds harmlessly on bacteria and other foodstuffs that are always present there, but sometimes, for reasons we do not understand, it becomes a dangerous parasite and begins invading the bowel wall, feeding on the tissues and red blood-cells and causing fever, pain and diarrhoea. This sudden bad behaviour by *Entamoeba histolytica* is more likely to occur in tropical and sub-tropical regions of the world, especially in unhygienic conditions. The disease that is caused in this way is called amoebic dysentery.

A pond amoeba

When *Entamoeba histolytica* leaves the body, it turns into a small, round object called a cyst. Such cysts do not move around by means of pseudopodia but contain 4 nuclei instead of 1 and are enclosed in a protective jacket. The *Entamoeba* cysts lie safely doing nothing in water or on the ground until taken in by another person through infected food or water. They can be carried onto food by flies. Once the cysts are inside a human being, their jackets dissolve, the 4 nuclei divide to make 8 and then the rest of the cell

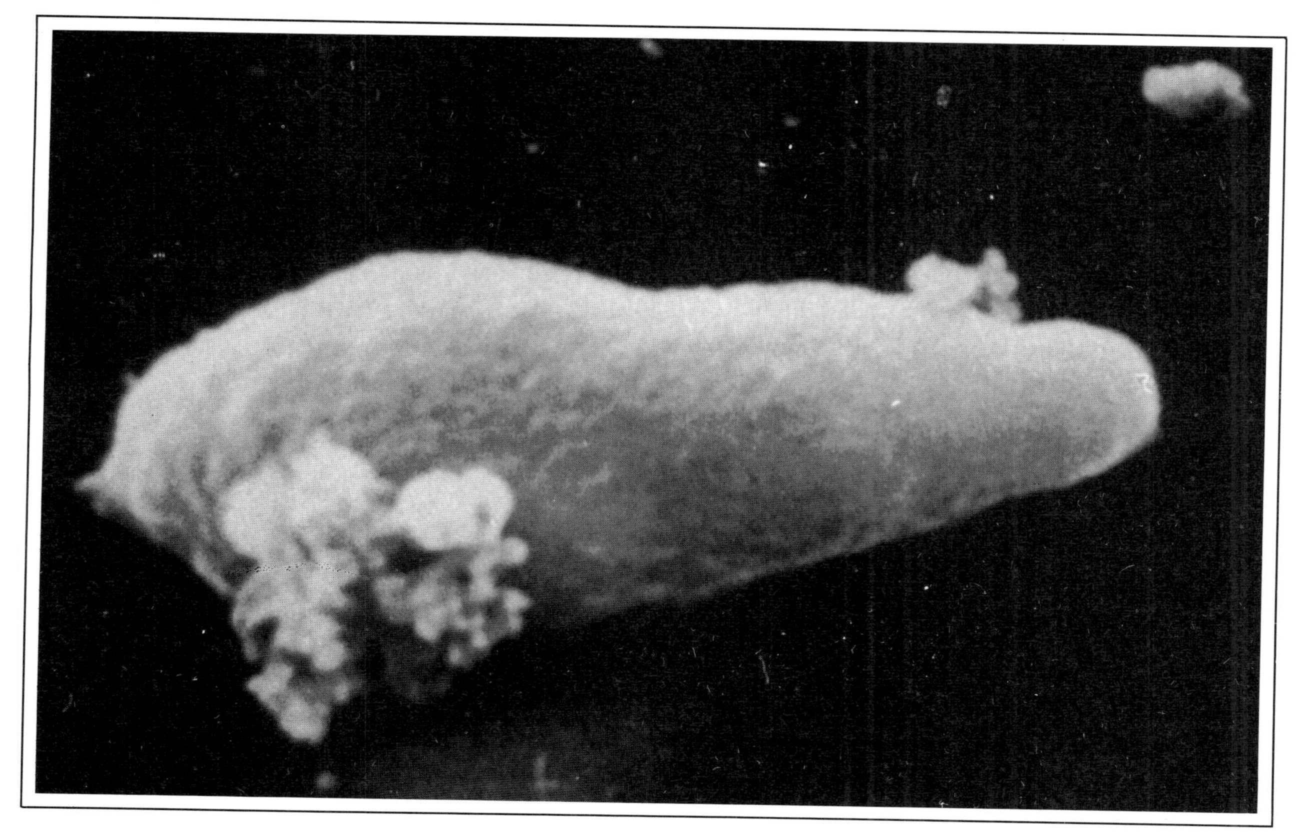

divides, producing 8 small amoebae which make their home in the intestine.
Amoebic dysentery can be cured nowadays with modern drugs, and prevention depends upon cleanliness and good hygiene. I have sometimes had to treat monkeys that have been infected by the *Entamoeba* parasite.

Entamoeba, a disease-maker

How we get amoebic dysentery

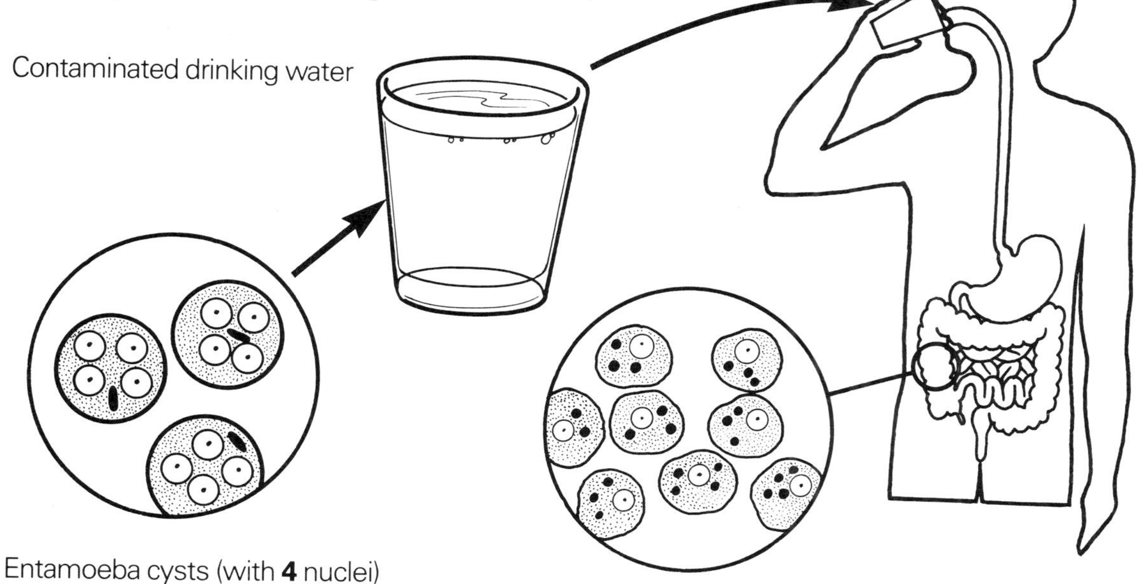

The Medicinal Leech

An animal that is now very rare in Britain but that, given the chance, would love to be a member of the zoo in you is the *medicinal leech*. You are most unlikely ever to see one in the wild, and the chances of one attaching itself to you are even smaller, but the medicinal leech is included here as the sort of rarity that might be found in some more exotic zoos.

Leeches are members of the great family of segmented worms called *Annelida*, which are soft-bodied animals without backbones. They live on land or water and breathe either through the skin or by means of gills (like fish). The body is divided into equal sections or segments and the skin of each segment sprouts bundles of horny bristles. The earthworm that lives in your garden is a typical Annelid.

Leeches are Annelids, but, unlike other members of the family, they do not have bristles. Their bodies always have 34 segments, they have suckers at both ends of the body, and they are all carnivorous or parasitic. They are 'hermaphrodites', having both female and male organs within the same body. Leeches live in fresh and salt water and on land, but all species need some water to survive, so they are not found in deserts, in the polar regions or higher than 4000 m above sea level. In the sea they are common parasites of fish, especially in the polar seas.

Leeches vary in length from about 5 mm to 45 cm, but their length and shape change frequently and dramatically, depending on whether their elastic muscular bodies are fully stretched out or not, and depending on how much food they have inside them. They can appear like long ribbons, or can take the shape of an egg, a leaf or pear. Some exotic leeches are brilliantly coloured, with wonderful skin-patterns. They go on growing for 5 years and can live for up to 20 years. Although some leeches eat earthworms and insect larvae, most are full-time or part-time parasites who attach themselves to living animals and suck blood and body juices.

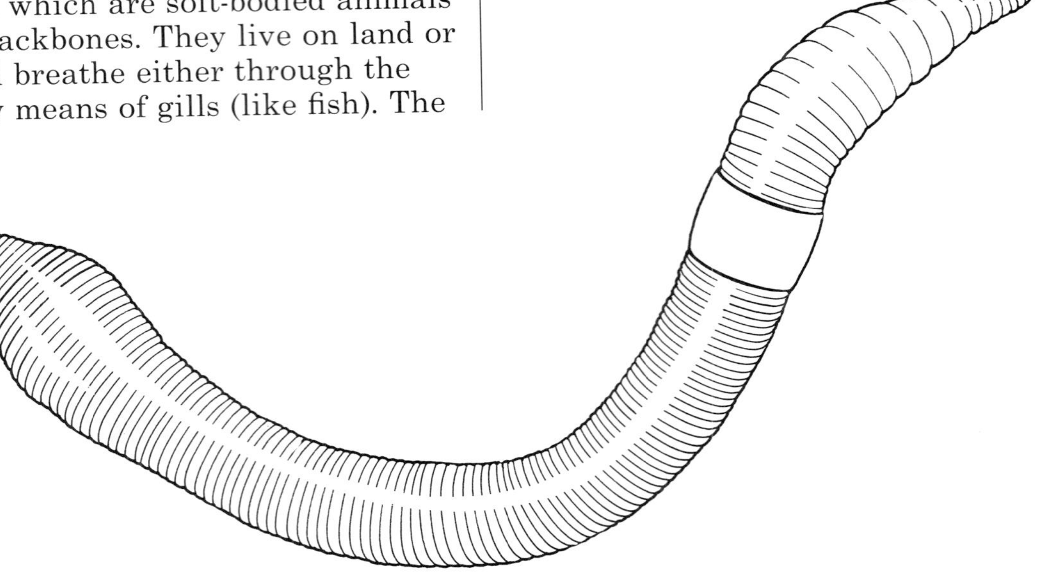

A typical annelid body-plan

The commonest leech in Britain is the *horse leech*, which lives in ponds, rivers and canals. It is a dark ribbon-like animal that feeds on fish, amphibians and the bodies of dead animals. Other

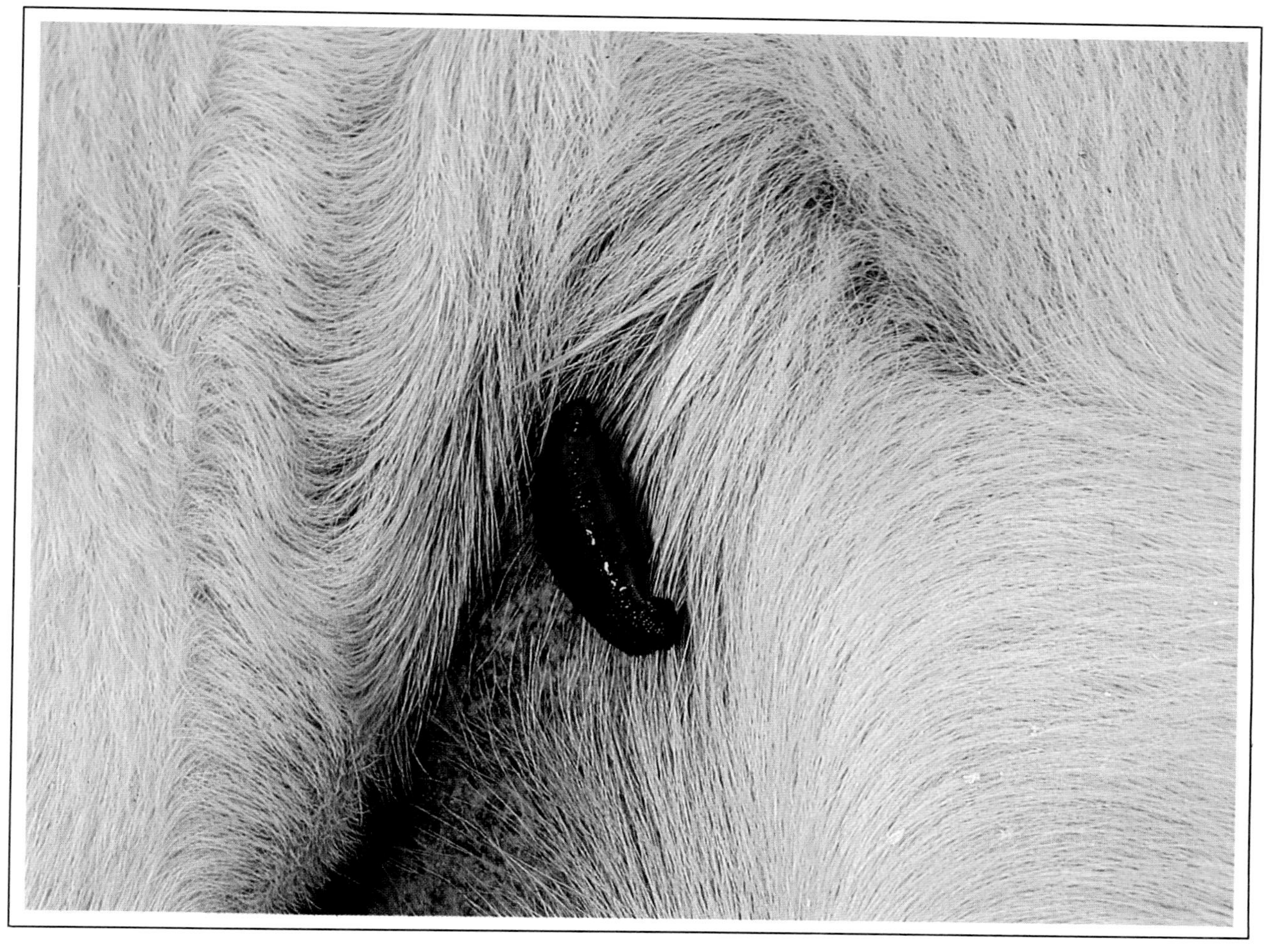

A leech on a calf's skin

leeches seek out birds that live around water, such as penguins and ducks, or reptiles such as crocodiles and turtles. I have often seen the tiny scars of old leech-bites around the tail of the hippopotamus. There are species that live in springs and wells and enter the noses and mouths of drinking animals. They fasten themselves to the walls of the air passages and grow rapidly, making it difficult for the animal to breathe and causing bleeding. In India such leeches injure large numbers of buffalo, cattle, horses and dogs.

In the hot, damp jungles and rain forests of the East, *land leeches* occur in vast numbers, hanging from the twigs and leaves of bushes and trees and lurking in the undergrowth. They keep themselves moist by urinating upon themselves! Alert and active, they quickly attach themselves to their prey and will work their way in unnoticed through the smallest opening.

The medicinal leech is an animal with a long and remarkable history. This handsome dark-olive-green leech with orange markings was once common in Britain, but is now found there only in the Lake District in northern England and in the New Forest in the south.

Detecting its prey at a distance by means of its 10 eyes, its sensitivity to movements in the water and by its ability to detect tiny amounts of chemicals, such as those in sweat, it swims with wave-like wrigglings of its body and attaches itself to the skin of its victims by means of its suckers. The front sucker contains mouth-parts, including a set of 3 extremely sharp cutting-blades. Each of these is rather like half of a circular saw, and the 3 are set at angles of 60° to one another, making a perfect Y shape. The blades rock to and fro, and cut usually painlessly and always very quickly through the skin (though when I have placed medicinal leeches on my hand to watch them feeding I have always felt a slight pin-prick as they went about getting their lunch!). The leech releases into the Y-shaped wound a special saliva that contains a chemical that stops blood from clotting. This substance, called 'hirudin' after the Latin name of the medicinal leech, *Hirudo*, is of great medical importance

Digestion can take many weeks and isn't done by the leech itself. Instead it is done by a colony of friendly bacteria that the leech carries in its intestines and which do all the work of breaking up the liquid food. A leech can survive happily on just one such meal per year. Medicinal leeches prefer to take the blood of warm-blooded animals such as humans, cattle or sheep.

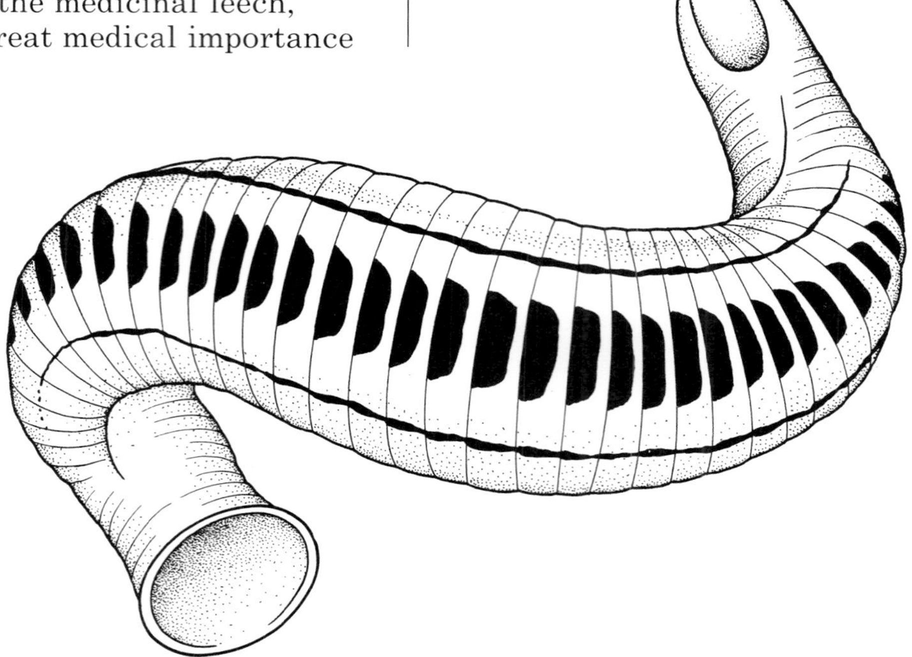

The medicinal leech

and has been studied and used by doctors for treatment of certain blood diseases in human beings. The leech saliva probably also contains some local anaesthetic, so that the victim feels no real pain. When the leech has made its cut it uses a muscular pump in its throat to draw out blood. Within a few minutes it is full and swollen up with about 6–7 cubic cm of blood and has changed from ribbon-shaped to roughly egg-shaped or pear-shaped. At this point it drops off its victim and sinks down in the water to digest its meal.

In olden days, when men and animals crossed rivers by walking through them or drank at ponds and riversides, it was easy for the medicinal leech to find its food. Changes in farming and the way people live have meant that cattle drink now at troughs in fields rather than from ponds, and men drive themselves and their livestock across rivers in trucks instead of on foot. Another important reason why there are now so few medicinal leeches is that in past centuries millions of them were caught for doctors to use in 'leeching' –

A leech dining on my arm

drawing blood off patients. This treatment was so common, right up to the middle of the nineteenth century, that doctors were themselves often called 'leeches'. Leeching was thought to be helpful in treating almost every illness, but we now know that in almost all cases it did no good at all. However, in a special situation where blood has to be drained from very delicate areas (for instance, around the eyes), surgeons will use the medicinal leech, whose delicate cutting mouthparts are finer than any surgeon's knife.

People used to make a living out of catching medicinal leeches. Girls would wade into ponds with their legs bare and pick of leeches as they came and stuck to them, putting them into little wooden barrels that they carried slung to their waists. Doctors kept their stocks of leeches in beautiful china jars.

Leeches have a number of natural enemies, including birds and fish, particularly the perch and trout. If you are ever lucky enough to see a medicinal leech, don't be put off by its vampire-like reputation. It is a fascinating and highly specialized sort of worm that has been used by man to play a major role in medicine over many centuries.

Leech girls collecting leeches

The Flea

An occasional inhabitant of the zoo in you is an insect that according to the Book of Samuel in the Bible caused the Philistines a lot of trouble, and that helped to kill a quarter of the population of Europe in the Middle Ages! This is the flea, a true but wingless insect which lives on the skin of its host as a parasite. Fleas possess a tough horny 'shell' covered with many bristly hairs. They have mouth-parts that are specially designed for piercing and sucking, and hind legs that enable the insect to make incredible jumps. Because fleas feed on the blood of mammals (including man) and birds, they sometimes carry infectious diseases. This is how the *rat flea* spread the Black Death in the Middle Ages, causing 25 million human beings to lose their lives – more people than died in any other known epidemic or war. In the Far East and other parts of the world, fleas are still involved in outbreaks of plague among man and animals. They carry the virus that causes the terrible disease myxomatosis among rabbits, and also the tapeworm parasites that infest dogs and cats.

There are 1600 species of flea in the world. They can be found in the Arctic and Antarctic, in tropical jungles, in deserts and in towns and cities. Most are 1–5 mm long. The largest British species is the *mole flea*, which reaches a length of 5–6 mm, while the largest known flea is one that was found in a beaver's nest in the United States and measured 8 mm.

Some fleas will only live on one kind of mammal or bird – for example the *shrew flea*, which doesn't fancy anything but shrews. Other fleas aren't so fussy; they prefer one kind of host but will sometimes feed on other species. *Cat fleas* prefer small cats, but will also visit humans, dogs, foxes and big cats, such as lions (Shakespeare wrote in *Henry V* about 'the valiant flea that dares eat his breakfast on the lips of a lion'). *Dog fleas* prefer dogs but can be found on humans or cats if dogs aren't available. The *human flea* prefers humans, but dogs and cats are also favourite hosts. The *chigoe* or *jigger*

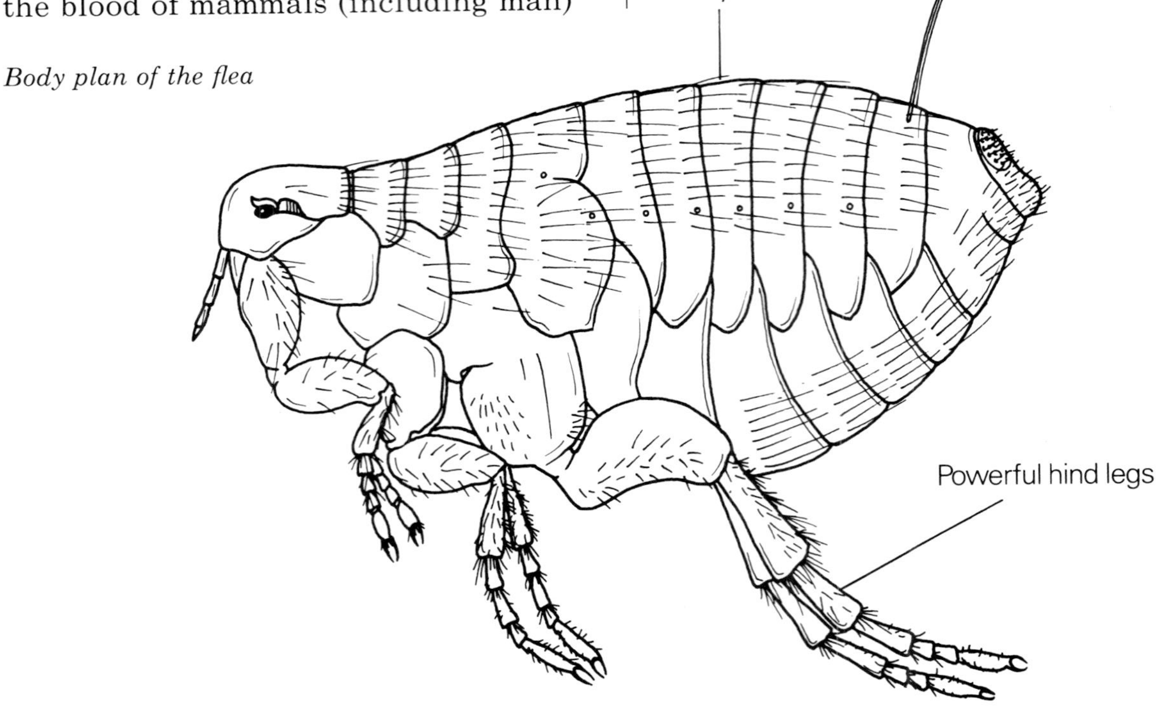

Body plan of the flea

flea, the smallest of all flea species, attacks humans, domestic animals and birds, and, while the male flea feeds on the surface of the skin, the female burrows beneath it and lives inside a little cyst or ball that grows around it. All fleas can cause itching and irritation of the skin as they feed, but the chigoe flea produces severe itching, burning and swelling, and is a serious pest in parts of tropical and sub-tropical America. Flea-bites on humans in northern Europe are generally quite harmless. They leave a small red dot surrounded by a light ring and are only slightly itchy. Apes and monkeys don't get fleas! Nor do horses and most hoofed animals. Rodents, on the other hand, have lots of fleas.

The human flea is 2–3 mm long and is red brown in colour and rather shiny. It lives for up to 2 years and can go a whole year without food, although it likes to feed every day if possible. Before mating, a female flea must have a meal of blood. Eggs are laid 4–8 at a time, with up to 400 laid over a period of

A cat flea on human skin

3 months on the body or in the bedding of the host. The eggs are white and oval but are not glued to hairs like those of lice. This means that they fall off the host's body very easily. The eggs hatch into tiny larvae in the form of grubs

Cat-flea eggs and droppings

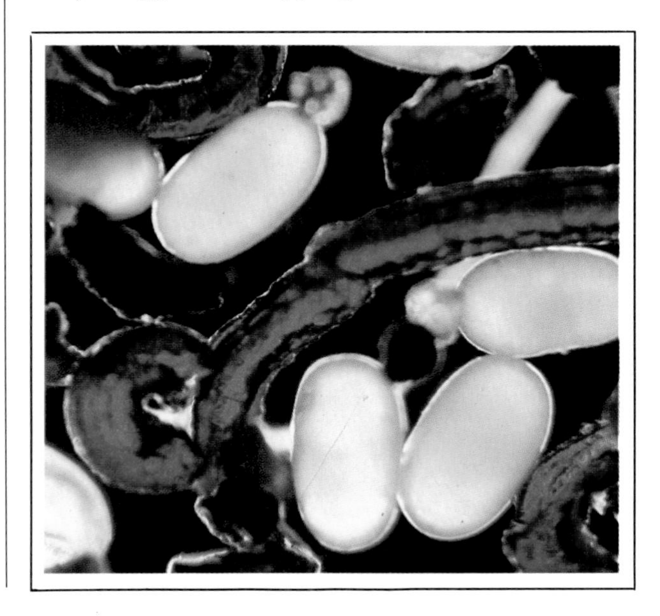

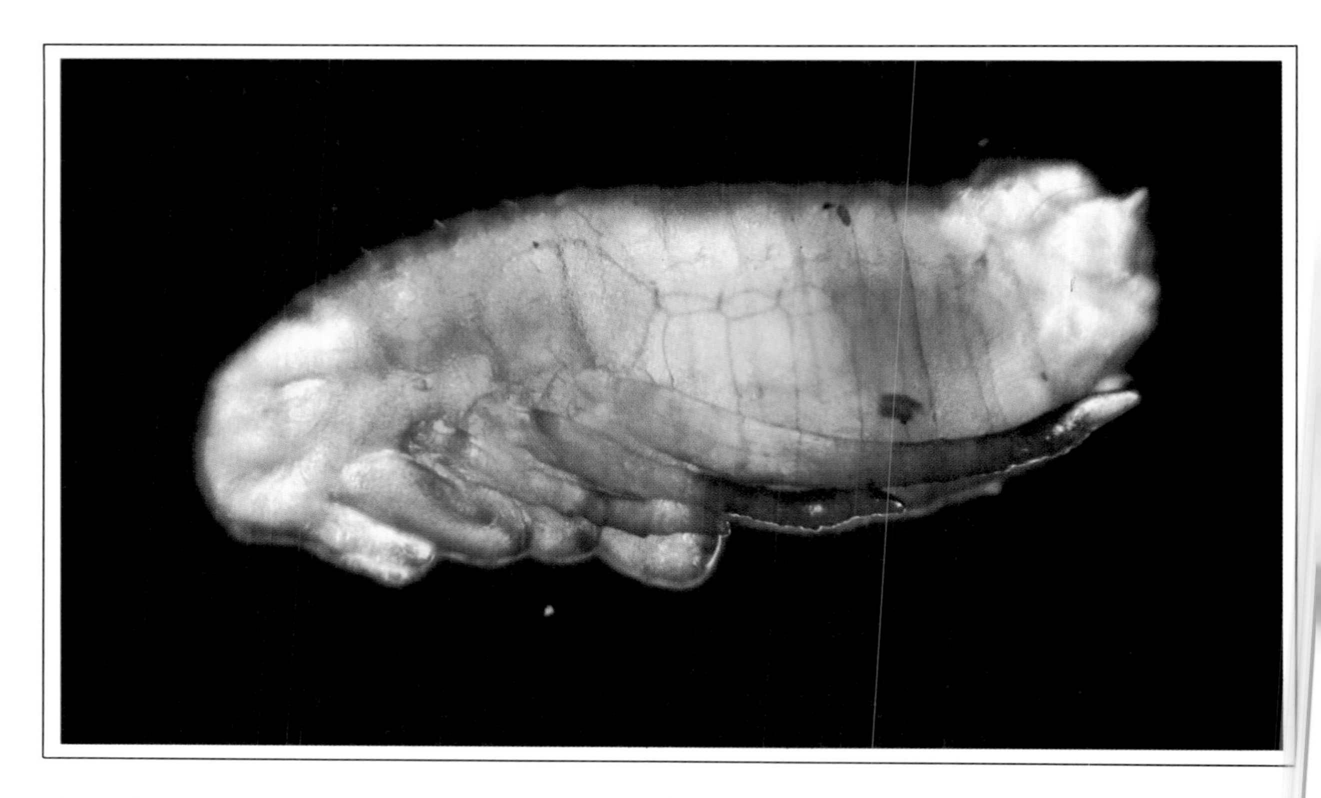

A cat-flea pupa

which feed on dried blood, waste products, skin-scales and the droppings of adult fleas (which contain blood, of course). After 1–3 moults, the larva spins a cocoon and turns into a pupa.

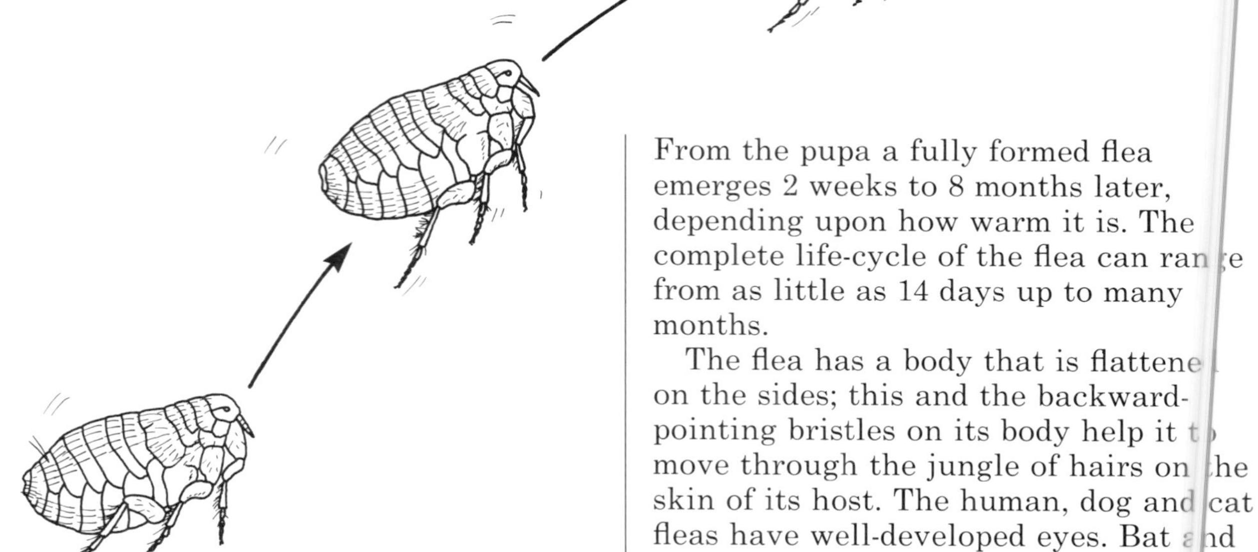

A champion jumper works out

From the pupa a fully formed flea emerges 2 weeks to 8 months later, depending upon how warm it is. The complete life-cycle of the flea can range from as little as 14 days up to many months.

The flea has a body that is flattened on the sides; this and the backward-pointing bristles on its body help it to move through the jungle of hairs on the skin of its host. The human, dog and cat fleas have well-developed eyes. Bat and mole fleas have poor eyes, or no eyes at

Roll up! The flea circus!

all, and so prefer hosts that live in the dark.

The flea's hind legs enable it to jump 200 times its own body length. One flea athlete achieved a high jump of almost 200 mm and a long jump of 330 mm. To do as well as the flea, a fairly tall human athlete would have to jump a quarter of a mile! The power for the flea's amazing jump does not come simply from flexing muscles but from the sudden pulling-in of a special elastic-like chunk of tissue that stores energy when resting.

I was fascinated as a boy by the 'flea circus' that used to be seen at Belle Vue Zoo in Manchester during the summer. (I saw another one a few years ago in Munich). In a flea circus, human fleas (other flea species don't perform so well) walk tightropes of fine hairs, 'fence' with swords made of thin wire, pull tiny carriages and carry umbrellas a few millimetres long. The audience watches the show through large magnifying lenses.

The behaviour of fleas, like that of so many other wild animals, has been used in the past as a means of forecasting the weather. An old British saying goes,

When eager bites the thirsty flea,
Clouds and rain you sure shall see.

The Louse

And now to the lousy part of the zoo! Lice are fascinating creatures, but they can be a great nuisance too, and are certainly not the most pleasant animals to have in your personal zoo. Because of this, I am glad to say that these little pests are not as common as they used to be.

One day, the Scottish poet Robert Burns was in church and saw a louse crawling over the bonnet of a lady sitting just in front of him. When he got home he wrote a poem called 'To a Louse'. Here is part of it, and, to make it easier for you if you don't understand Scottish words, I shall repeat it afterwards in ordinary English.

Ye ugly common creepin', blastit
  wonner,
Detested, shunn'd by saunt an' sinner!
How daur ye set your fit upon her,
  Sae fine a lady?
Gae somewhere else, and seek your
  dinner
On some poor body.

You ugly, common, creeping useless
  creature,
Detested, shunned by saint and
  sinner!
How dare you set your feet upon her,
  So fine a lady?
Go somewhere else, and seek your
  dinner
On some poor person.

Lice are wingless insects with flattened bodies and are 0.3–11 mm long. They come in various colours, from white or yellow to brown or black.

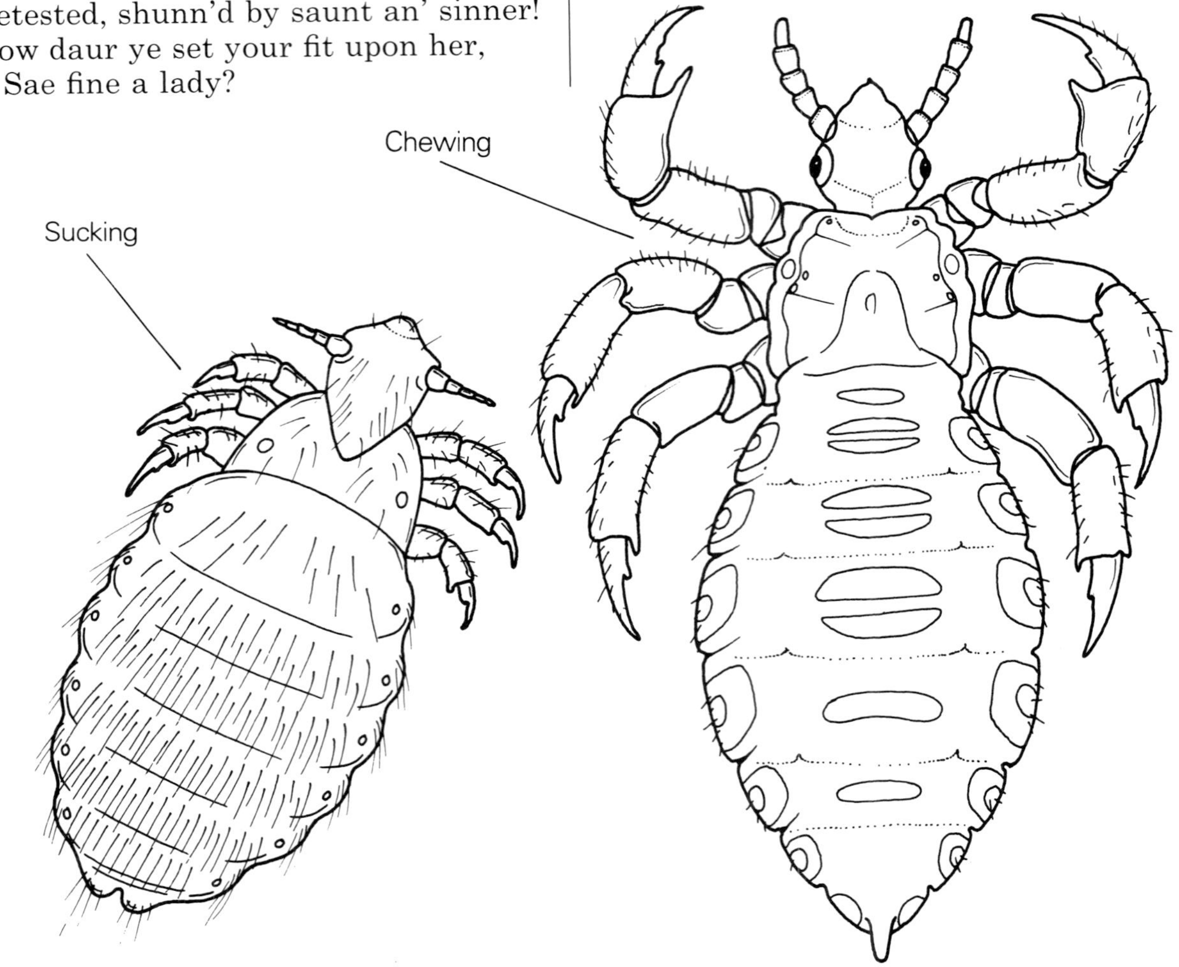

Sucking and chewing lice

There are two main types: *chewing lice*, which live on the bodies of mammals and birds and eat skin-scales, feathers, hair and grease, and *sucking lice*, which suck blood. There are almost 3000 species of chewing lice and about 400 species of sucking lice known to science.

Each species of chewing louse lives on a particular type of animal. For instance, *elephant lice* live on elephants and *lemur lice* live on lemurs. Some animals, such as bats, ant-eaters, armadillos and whales, don't have any lice.

Sucking lice are pests that are sometimes found on human beings and can carry diseases such as typhus in tropical countries. They feed only on warm blood and die within 12–72 hours if they don't get it (unlike fleas, which can go without a meal for as long as a year). Each of their feet has a single big claw which they use to grasp the hairs of the host creature. The hold of the claws is amazingly powerful – a louse can resist a pull of 1 kg! Even if the body is cut from the head, the louse continues sucking for a while, and it can survive under water for a long time. (When a seal dives, *seal lice* take air down with them, trapping it between their scales and hairs.)

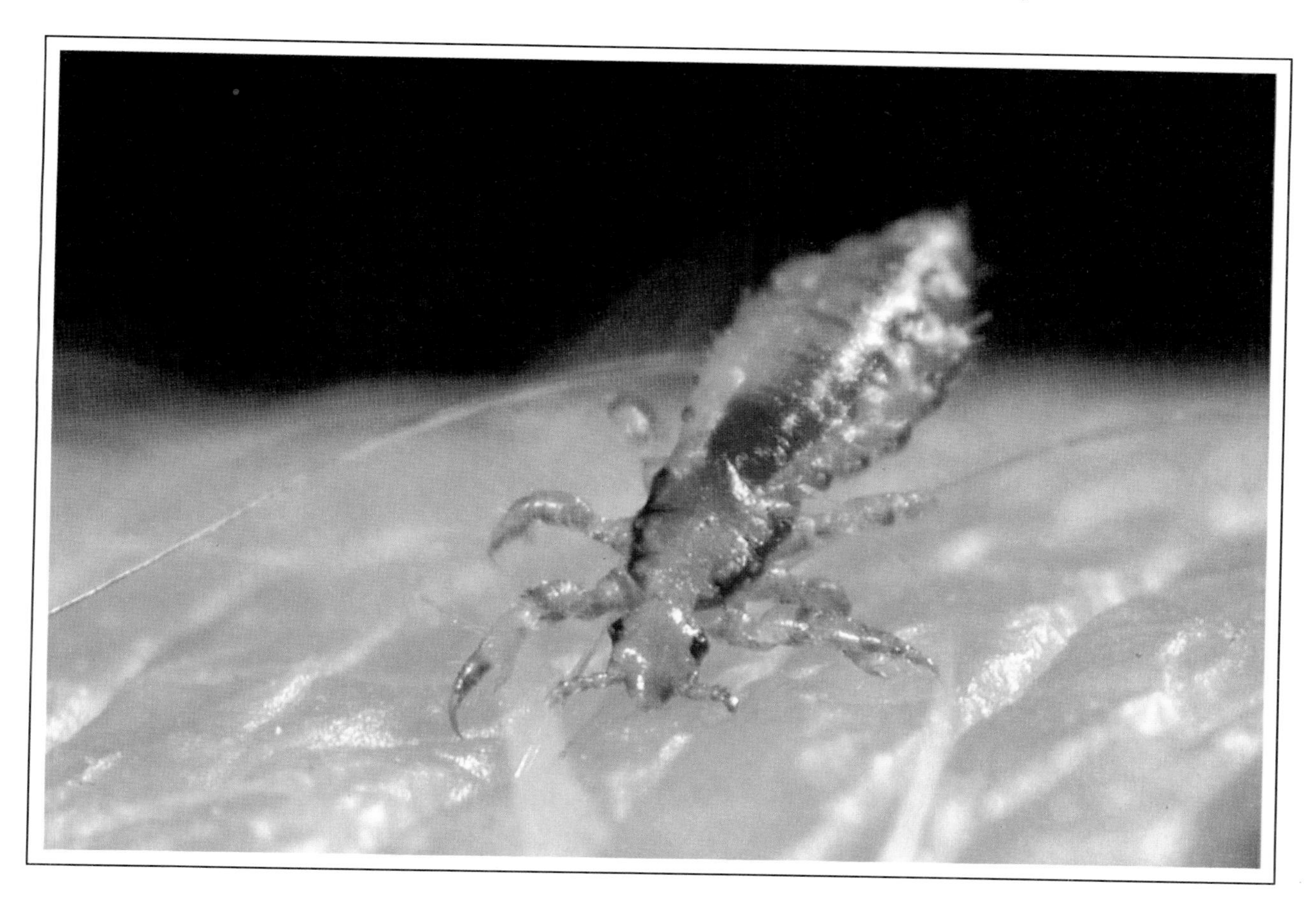

An adult head louse on my hand

As with chewing lice, specific kinds of sucking lice live on specific hosts. Some prefer rodents, others elephants, others man and the great apes. White birds have white body-lice, while black birds have black ones. Many animals and birds carry several species of louse at the same time, with each species living on one particular part of the body. Lice are attracted by the heat given out by a living animal and will walk towards a

A sucking louse at lunch

body when they can sense its warmth. This they are able to do from a distance of up to 30 cm. Probably the smell of their particular host also attracts them. They also get about by travelling on clothing, on the wind or by hitching a ride on flying insects. As soon as they come into contact with an object, lice automatically try to climb up it.

Three kinds of louse live on humans: one likes to live in the pubic hair of the groin area (at the front, where your legs join); the second prefers the body hair, including that of the eyebrows and beard; and the third makes its home in the hair of the head. People used to think that lice came out of nowhere, created out of nothing. It was also commonly held that only strong, fit people produced lice – that they were a sure sign of good health! In the olden days lice were used in folk medicine, and as late as the last century people in the Lake District in the north of England believed that, if they swallowed a tablespoonful of live headlice, that would cure jaundice (a kidney disease in which the skin turns yellow). In the seventeenth century witches were sometimes accused of sending lice to people that hadn't suffered from them before, as a way of bewitching them. In 1645, a woman called Alice Warner who lived in Suffolk in the east of England confessed that she had sent evil spirits to carry lice to two women who had annoyed her. Sadly, the courts believed this nonsense and she was convicted.

The sucking louse has a needle-like sucking-tube (proboscis) in its mouth-parts. When not in use, it is pulled back into the head. When sucking, the proboscis is extended and drilled deep into the skin, while the louse literally stands on its head! Head lice have even adapted themselves to the different hair characteristics of various human races. The differences are in the shape of their claws. Some have claws that fit perfectly the hair-shafts of white people; others have evolved to grasp the slightly differently shaped hairs of black people; and yet others have evolved to live in the hair of yellow-skinned people.

the egg-cap to one side and jets them out of the egg!

These days, outbreaks of lice infestation occur from time to time in places where lots of people are in close contact. For example, such outbreaks sometimes occur in schools. The lice are a nuisance, but they can easily be got rid of by using special shampoos that kill the lice and the nits.

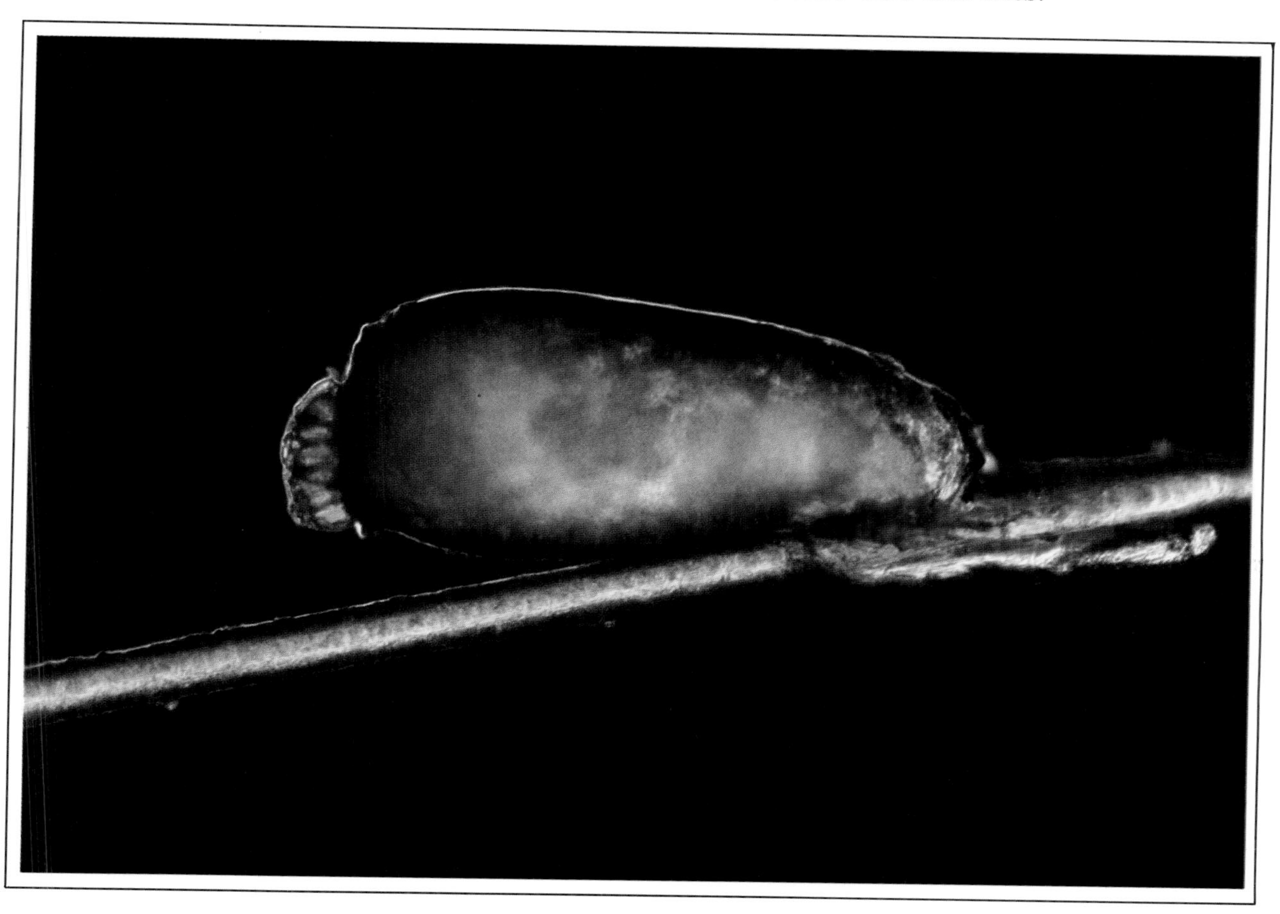

A nit stuck to a human hair

Lice lay eggs called 'nits' and glue them to the hairs of the host. Each egg has a lid in it which is fitted with air-holes. Up to 300 eggs are laid over a period of around 6 weeks. The larvae, tiny copies of adult lice, hatch after 1–2 weeks. They cut their way out of the egg using an egg tooth on the head. They then swallow air, as well as any liquid remaining in the egg, and in this way puff themselves up. Some of the mixture of fluid and air is then pushed out of their rear ends, and this pushes

Some primitive tribes people actually treat lice as sacred and precious. When the Spaniards conquered South America, Indians would often bring them purses full of their own body-lice.

Some animals live by preying on lice. In the Mediterranean area, some lizards survive on the lice to be found in colonies of seagulls, and others do the same among the cormorants that live along the coast of Peru.

The Roundworm

The world is overflowing with round little worms, and some of them are occasionally to be found in human beings. I'm not referring to earthworms, those familiar garden creatures that live in the soil and have segmented bodies, but to another and even bigger group of worms, whose bodies are not divided into segments. These worms are whitish or translucent (light can pass through them) and usually tube-shaped. They vary in size from a fraction of a millimetre to over 8 m long! These giants live in the Pacific Ocean.

About 20,000 species of *nematode*, as scientists call this type of creature, have been identified. The earliest ones lived over 370 million years ago. Many, mainly the tiniest ones, are 'free-living' and do not rely on other things to provide them with food and lodgings, but can be found in both fresh and salt water, in soil, moss and decaying matter. Others are wholly or partially parasitic on plants and animals. One little worm, only 1 mm long, is called the 'vinegar eel'. It lives its whole life in beer-barrels, where it feeds on the yeast used to make beer from hops and water.

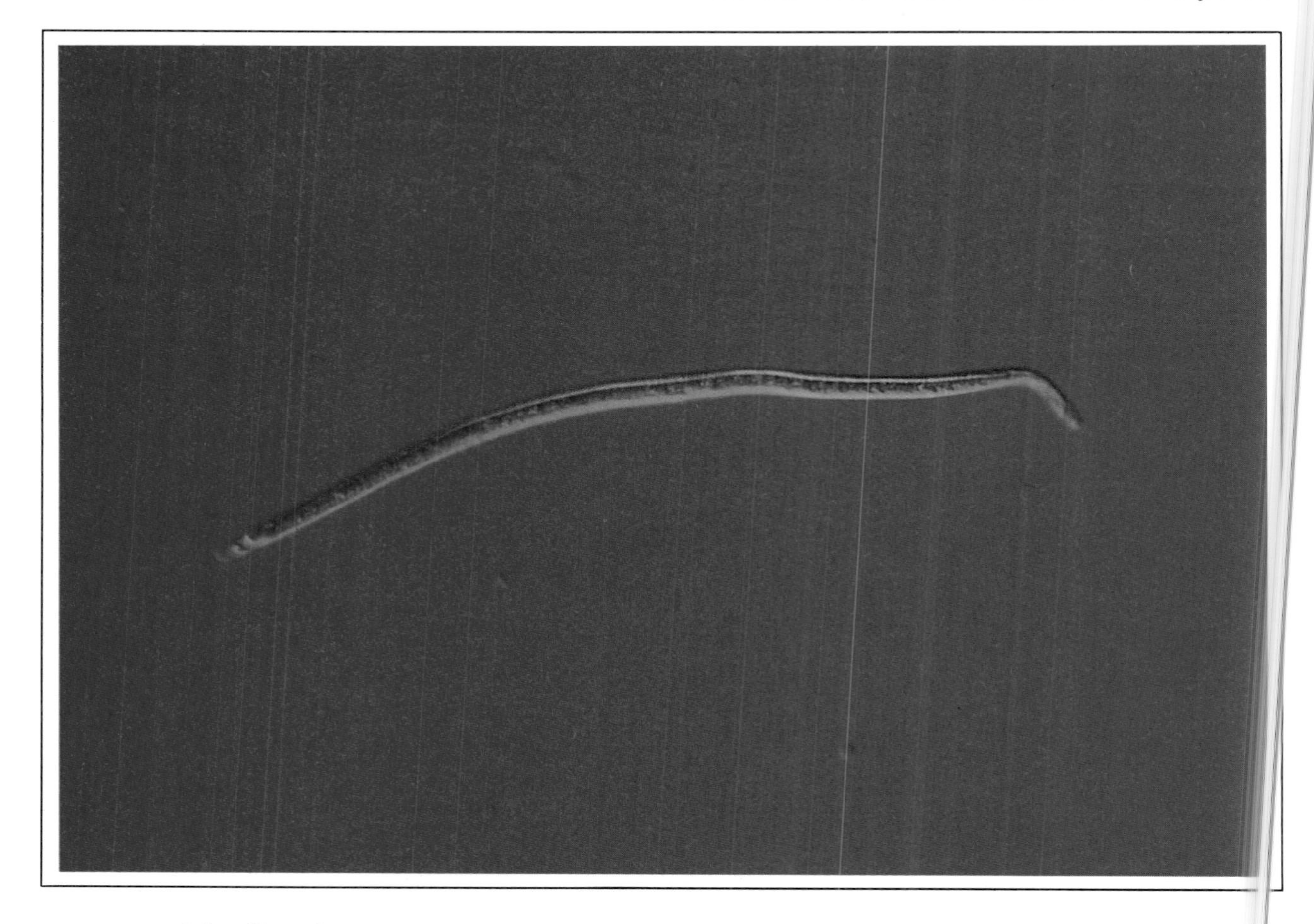

A typical roundworm or nematode

It is amazing to think that the soil can contain as many as 100 million nematodes per square metre, and they are one of the largest groups of living creatures in the world. There are millions of them, and they can be found just about everywhere. It is said that if all the buildings and other man-made structures on earth, along with all the trees and the rest of the plant life, were suddenly made to vanish, an outline of all of them would remain. For a moment, familiar things and places would still exist in a sort of ghostly form made up of the innumerable nematode worms that inhabit them. 'Houses' of worms, 'trees' of worms, 'fences' and 'bushes' and 'telegraph poles' of worms would all be visible, their shape outlined by these tiny yet wonderfully abundant worms.

The most troublesome roundworms are those that, as parasites of man and animals, can cause disease. Some free-living nematodes also attack the roots, stems and leaves of food plants and are considered a great pest by farmers. In hot countries hundreds of millions of people are infected by species of roundworm, mainly because not enough care is taken to make sure that food and water supplies are free of these pests. In Europe and America, farmers have to keep a watchful eye on roundworms that can invade the bodies of cattle, sheep, pigs, chickens and turkeys, and you probably know that pet cats and dogs have to be 'wormed' from time to time – given a special powder to get rid of similar troublesome parasites that infect them.

Human beings in Europe and America are not often infected with roundworms, but several species do sometimes cause trouble. The *pin worm* is one of them, and its life-cycle is typical of that of many roundworm parasites.

Pin worms are parasites of human beings, apes and some other animals. They are sometimes found living in the bowel or large intestine of children, and usually do not cause illness or injury in any way. Male pin worms are 2–5 mm long and are seen only rarely, while females are 8–13 mm long and whitish pink in colour. After being fertilized by the male, the female travels down the large intestine to the anus, through

A pin worm's life-cycle

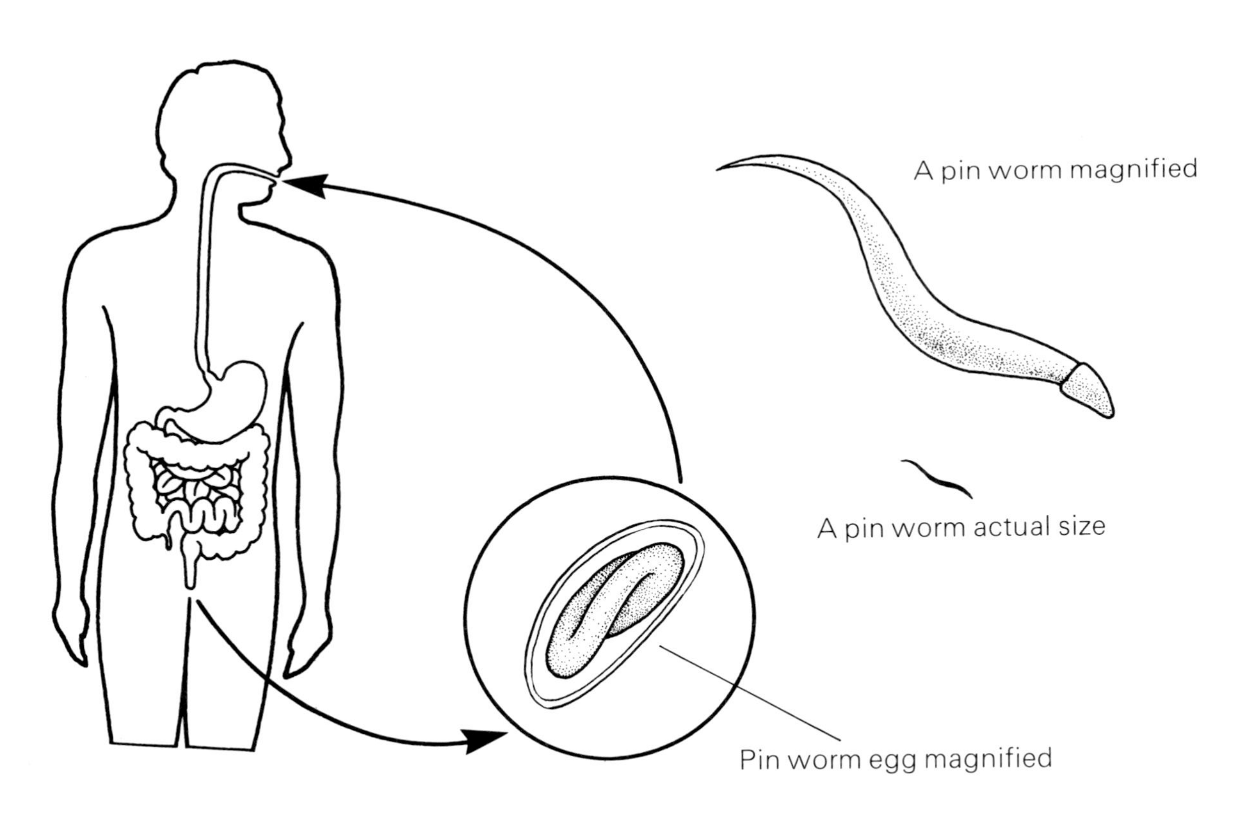

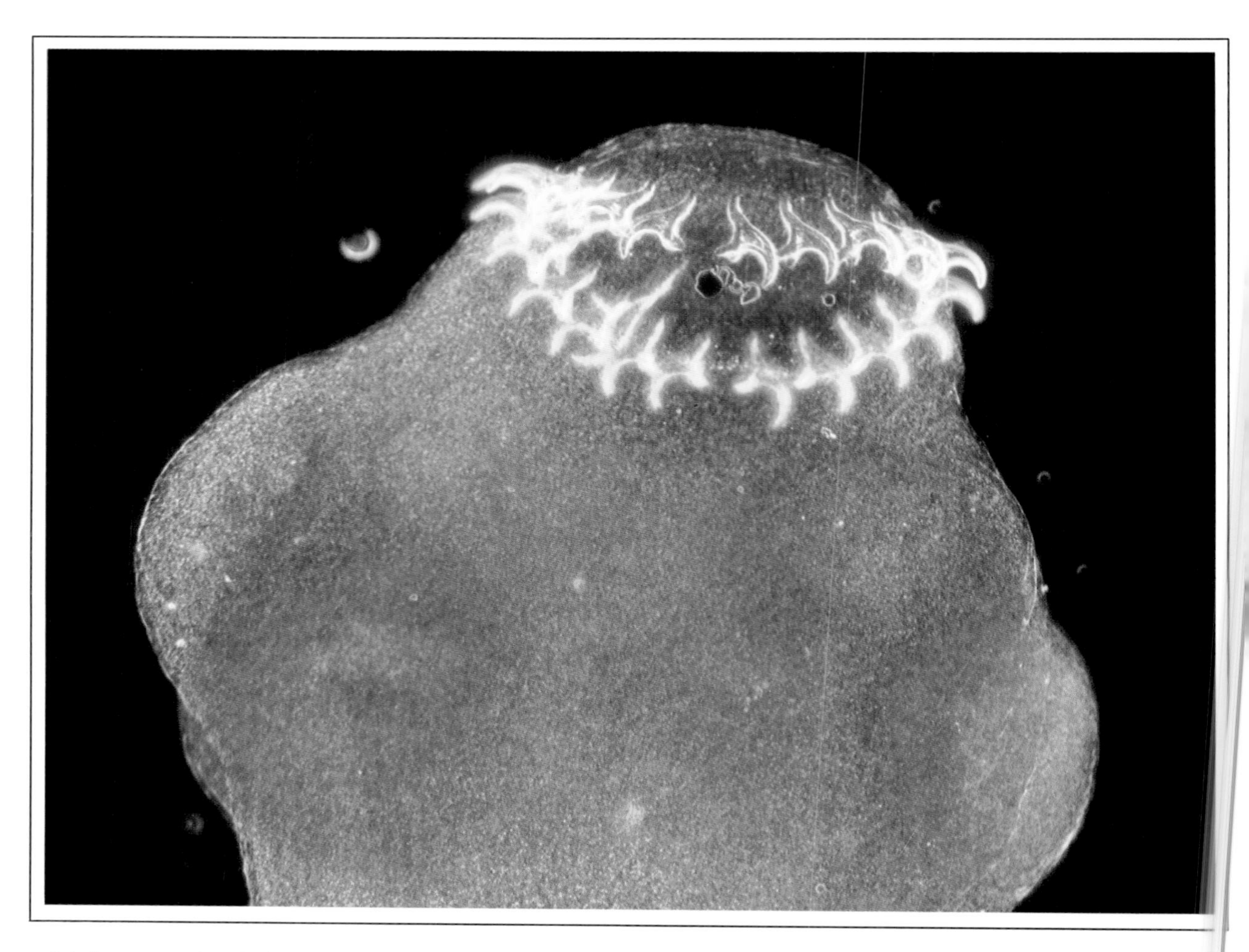

which your body's waste products pass out when you go to the toilet. When she gets there, she pops out and lays her eggs on the skin nearby. If you scratch this area and do not wash your hands, it is easy to carry the eggs or the larvae that hatch from them to the mouth, where they are swallowed and pass down into the large intestine. The full life-cycle takes between 2 and 6 weeks to complete. This worm spreads with great ease from one member of a family to another, and doesn't only infect people who don't keep themselves clean and tidy. Fortunately, modern medicines kill the worm rapidly and soon put an end to any infection.

Some roundworms such as the pin worm just feed on food around them in the bowel. Others actually suck blood from the wall of the bowel, and there are some dangerous species whose life-

The head of a tapeworm

cycles include wandering journeys by the larvae through the deep body tissu of the liver, where important damage can be caused.

Two other major classes of worm ca sometimes infect human beings. The first, the *tapeworm*, is a parasite whos body is flat and ribbon-like and composed of a tiny head attached to a chain of compartments that look a bit like the segments of segmented worm such as earthworms but are actually separate units joined together. Each segment or 'proglottid' contains mass es of eggs. The life-cycle of the tapewor n is not as simple as that of the pin wo m. To develop properly, the larvae must find temporary hosts such as pigs or fish. Man is infected by eating pork hat has not been cooked long enough or by eating raw fish. (Raw fish is a food often eaten in a number of countries, including the Scandinavian countries and Japan.)

The second class of worms, rare in humans, is the *fluke worm* – a leaf-shaped parasite that, like the tapeworm, has a complicated life-style and needs temporary hosts for its larvae. Snails are often hosts of fluke-worm larvae. The fluke worm is a serious parasite of sheep, in which it mainly attacks the liver. I often see another kind of fluke worm living fairly harmlessly in the stomach of dolphins.

Roundworms are quite long-lived. Many species reach 15 years of age, and there are reports that some nematodes that live as parasites on plants can live for as long as 39 years.

In the seventeenth century, the Dutchman Anton van Leeuwenhoek was the first man to use a microscope to study some of the tiny living creatures in his own body and in the world around him.

After examining vinegar-eel nematodes he wrote,

'I have had several gentlewomen in my house, who were keen on seeing the little eels in vinegar; but some of them were so disgusted at the spectacle that they vowed they'd never use vinegar again. But what if one should tell such people in future that there are more animals living in the scum on the teeth in a man's mouth, than there are men in a whole kingdom?'

A typical fluke worm

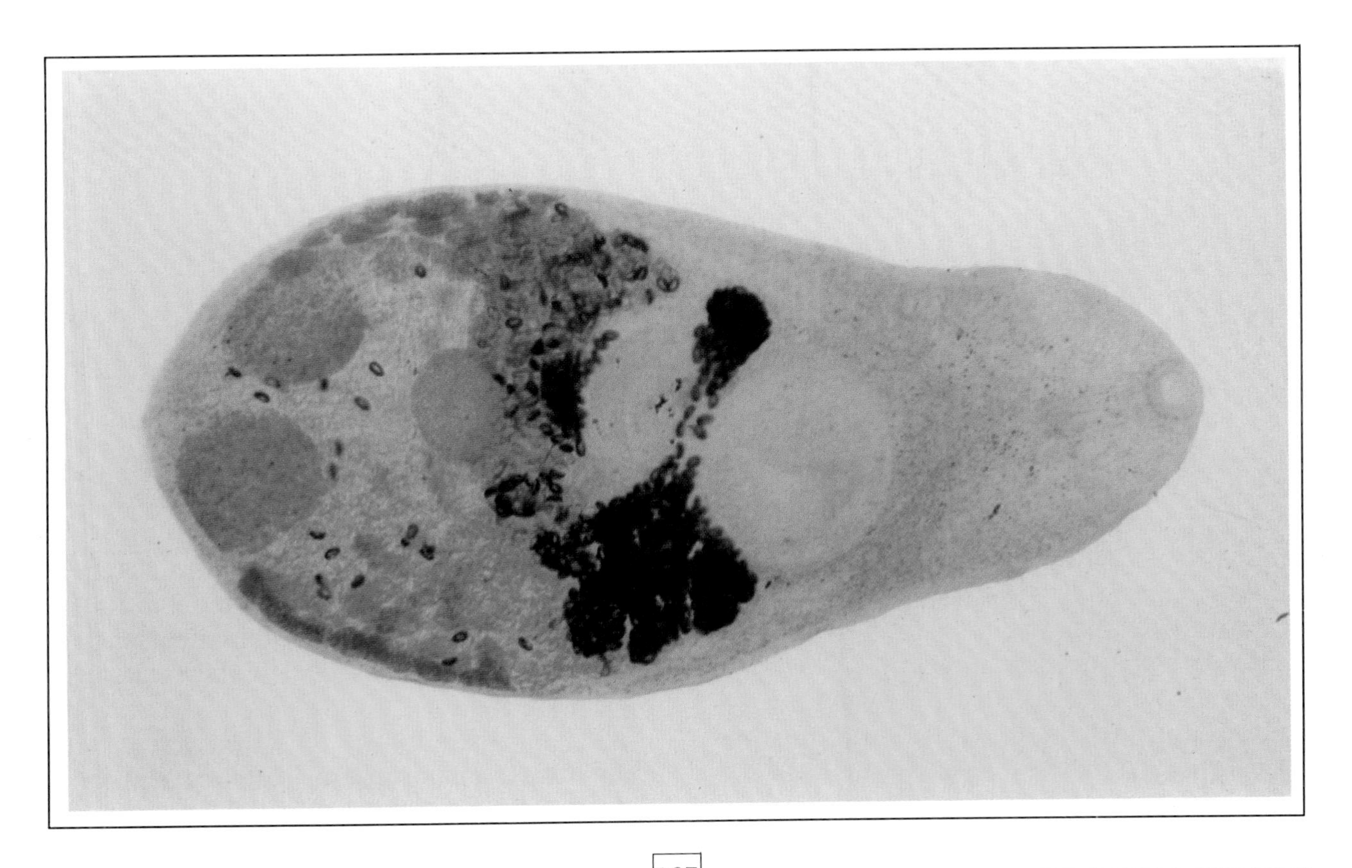

The Mite

In your skin, particularly that of the eyelids, some distant relatives of the scorpion are living at this very moment. These are the mites, members of the family of animals called *Arachnida*, which includes scorpions and spiders. Unlike insects, they have 8 legs, not 6. Some mites live in the sea, others on land. They can be found from the Arctic to the Antarctic. Some, such as the ones that belong to the zoo in you, are parasites, and are the smallest of all arthropods (creatures with joints in their legs) known to science.

Mites that burrow into the skin of mammals and birds cause a disease called 'mange' ('scabies' in humans) by feeding on scurf and skin-scales and sucking blood. Some mites cause only a little damage, wandering about through the dried upper layers of the skin. Other species burrow deep into the skin and cause serious swelling and burning. Some prefer to live in animals' outer ears, and are a common pest among pet cats and dogs. Mites that affect some kinds of birds can even penetrate deep into the body, reaching the lungs and air-sacs, though in fact they don't cause much trouble when they get there. Some mites lodge in the body-surface of man and other animals without attracting any attention.

One of these is called *Demodex*. It is your constant companion, always to be found in your personal zoo. Only about

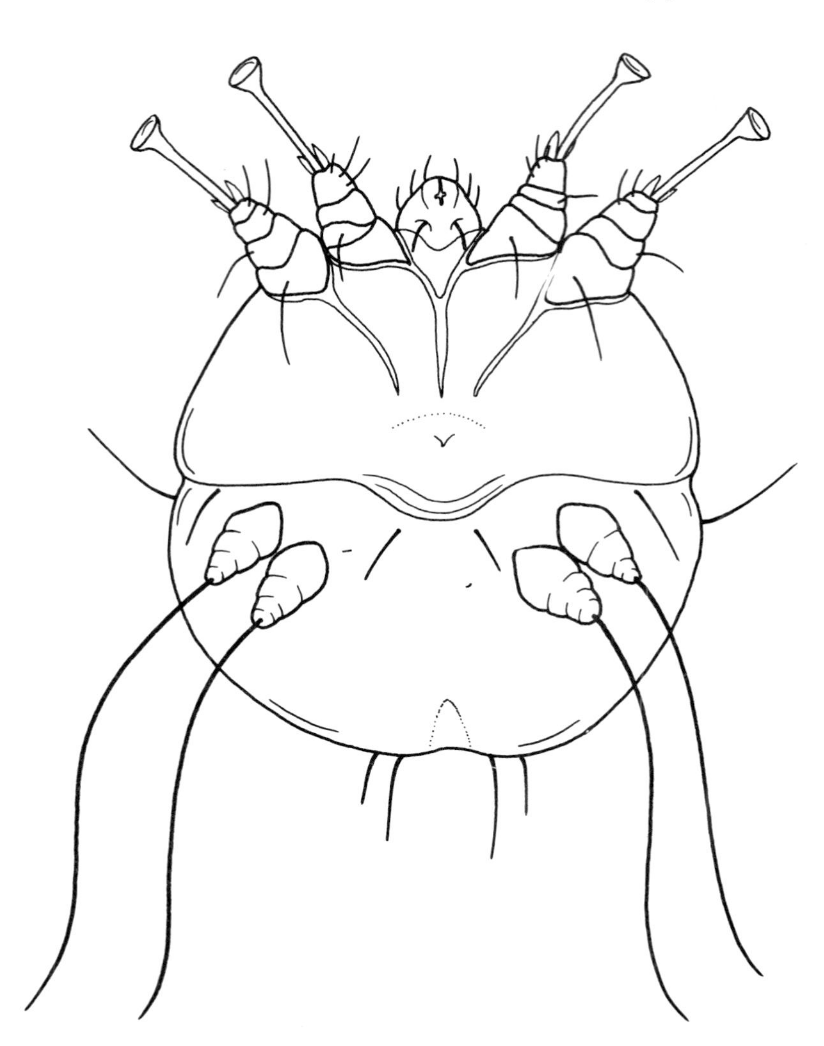

The mite's body-plan

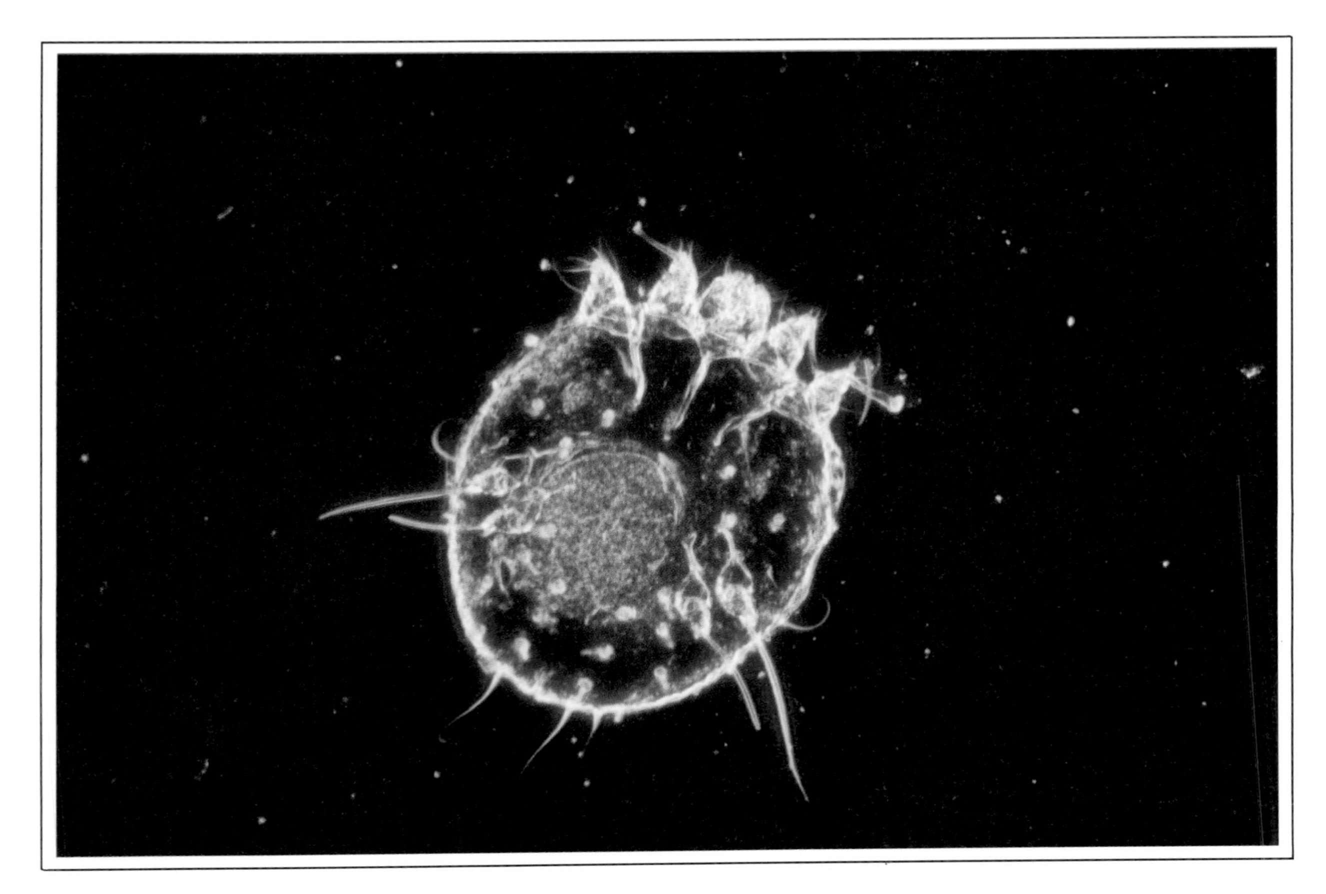

Sarcoptes, a mite that causes mange

0.3 mm long and shaped like a cigar, it has short, sucker-like legs and is usually found lying head-down in hair follicles (the little pockets from which hair grow), squeezed between the hair and the follicle wall. In this position it scarcely moves, but it can, if it wants, march at a speed of around 375 mm per hour. It is particularly fond of the eyelids and the follicles from which the eyelashes spring. As many as 25 mites have been found down one human eyelash follicle! A normal 'population' of mites in your eyelids is about 1–2 for every 16 lashes.

Mites of both sexes are to be found in the hair follicles. Mating occurs close to the entrance to the follicle. About 10–15 hours later, the female descends and lays her eggs in the grease-secreting gland under the follicle. The eggs are only about 0.075 mm long and are heart-shaped. After 2–3 days they hatch and the larvae emerge from them looking something like the adult mite but

Demodex loves eyelids

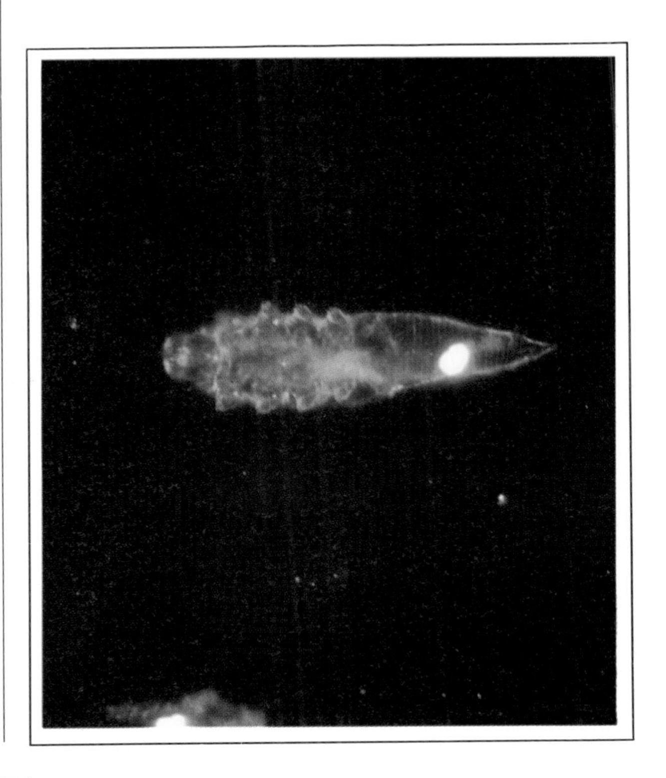

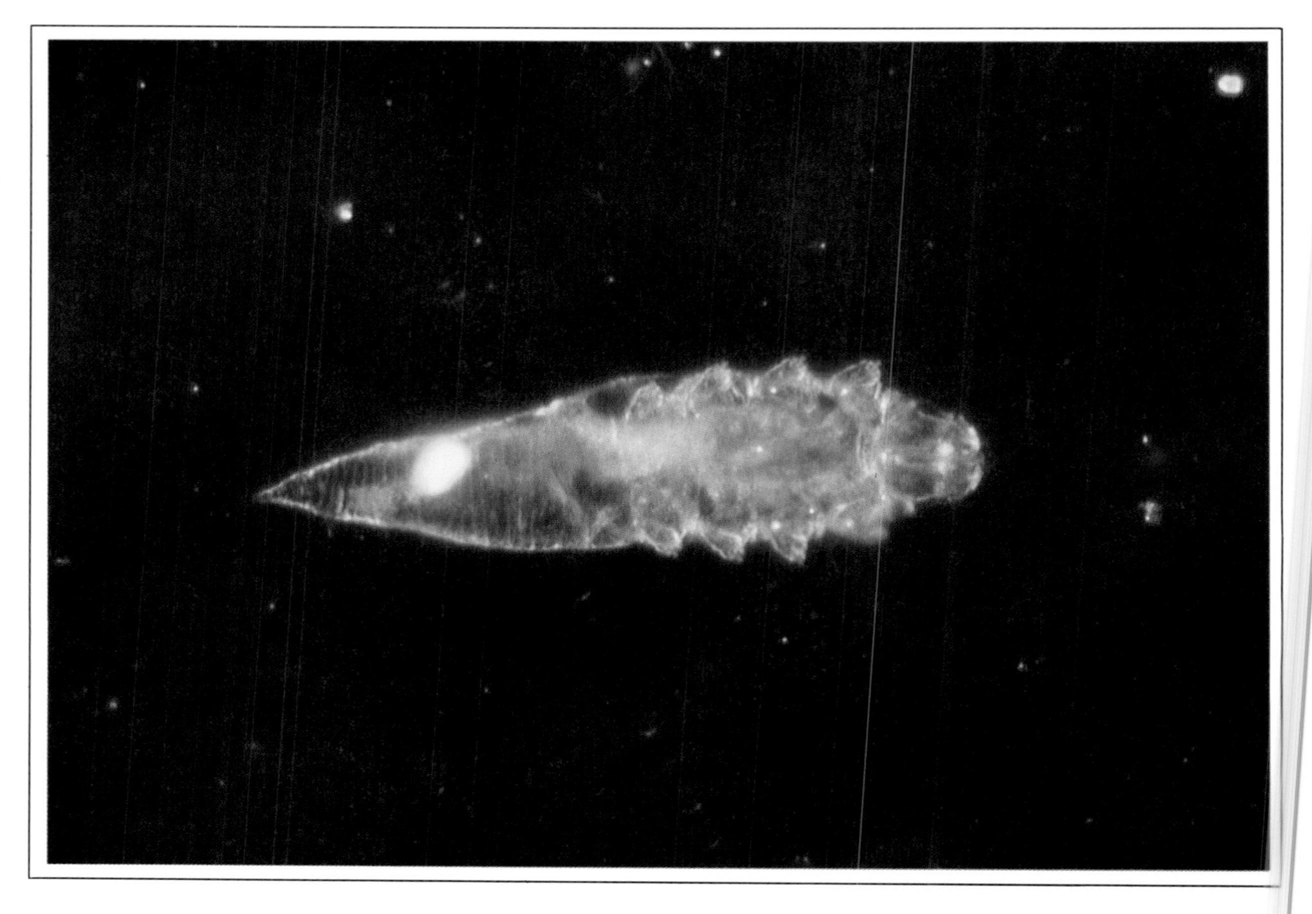

The eyelash mite, Demodex

having only 6 legs. These larvae shed their outer casing after around 2 days to produce an 8-legged 'protonymph', which in turn moults its shell after a further 3 days to become a 'deutonymph'. This creature has weak legs and cannot keep a firm hold of the hair, so it gets washed to the surface of the skin with the grease from the gland under the follicle. The poor little thing is then obliged to wander about on the surface of the skin for a day or so before finding a follicle into which it squeezes and in which it moults again to become an adult mite. The total lifespan of a mite is about 2 weeks.

Sarcoptes is the name of a mite that often causes mange in animals and occasionally produces a similar complaint called scabies in humans. At about 0.4 mm long, it is slightly bigger than Demodex, and also has a different shape: under the microscope it looks rather like a tiny tortoise. Sarcoptes digs into skin using the front two pairs of legs, which have cutting blades fixed to their 'knees'. The backward-facing spines on the body also help it to burrow, which it does at around 3 mm per day. As the female tunnels, she lays 2–3 eggs every day. These eggs are oval and white, and as many as 30 of them can often be found dotted behind the female along her burrow. This digging in the skin causes itching and burning, and scratching can introduce germs into the skin and set up bacterial infections. Mange and scabies are successfully treated by doctors and vets nowadays. Sheep are dipped in special solutions to prevent mange, and humans and other creatures can be treated by special shampoos, creams, sprays and even tablets.

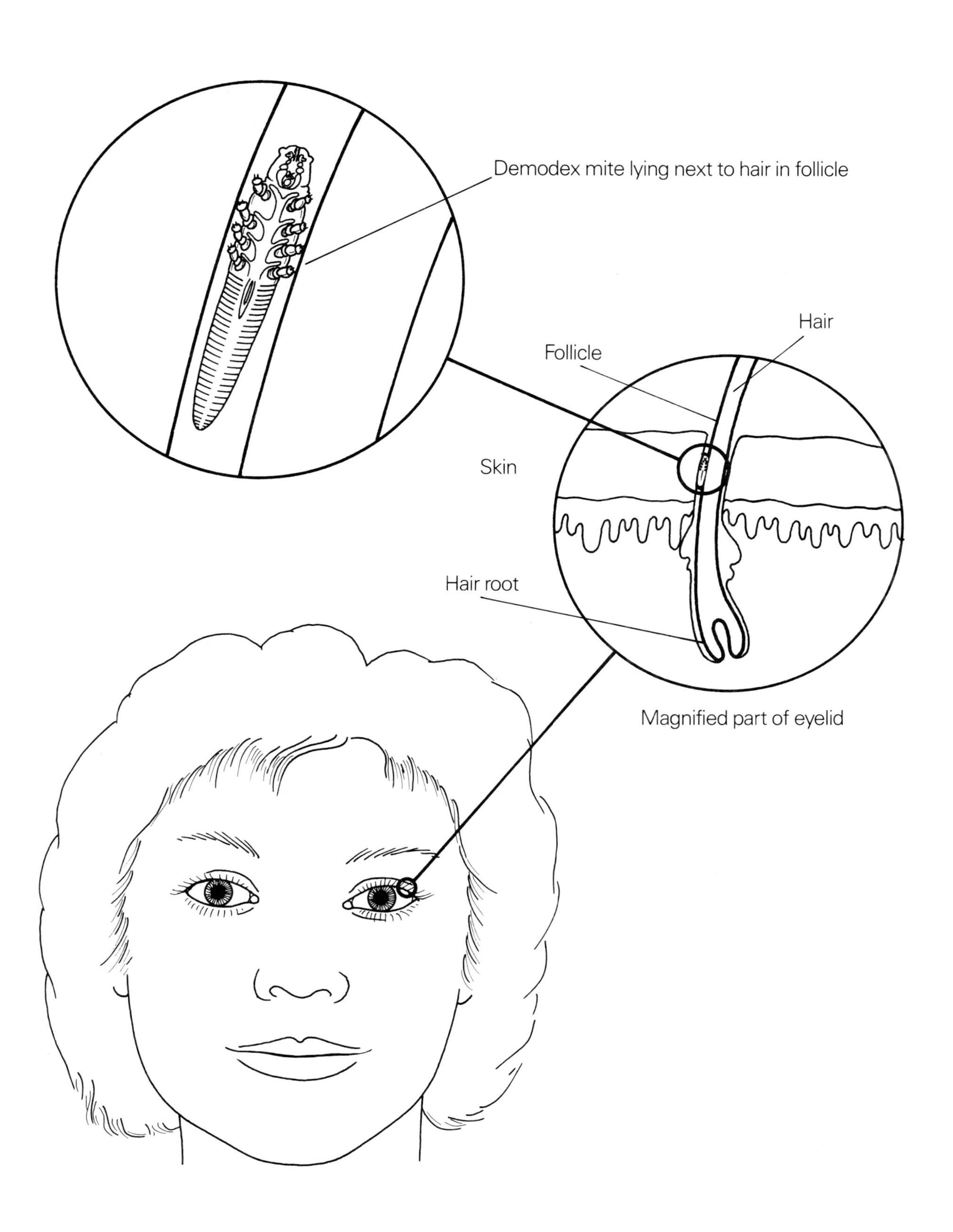

The mite that lives in eyelids

The Malaria Parasite

We have already looked at the amoeba, a form of protozoan animal that lives commonly in the intestines of human beings and is usually harmless. Another kind of protozoan can live in humans, finding a home with the red cells of the blood. It causes a disease that is no longer native to Europe, and does not normally occur outside the tropics, but which has been responsible directly or indirectly for *half* of all human deaths since the Stone Age. This protozoan, a mere dot when viewed under a high-power microscope, is the malaria parasite, which still kills at least 1 million people each year in Africa and Asia. Other animal species, such as apes, monkeys, birds (particularly penguins) and reptiles, can suffer from kinds of malaria.

Malaria in man is transmitted by mosquitoes of a particular group called *Anopheles*. 3 species of Anopheles mosquito, capable of carrying malaria, live in Britain, but can only carry the disease if they happen to come into contact with someone who already has it. No natural cases of malaria have occurred in Britain since the 1940s. Before that, soldiers returning from fighting abroad in the First World War (1914–18) had brought back the disease with them, and malaria-carrying mosquitoes made their home in marshes not far from London. Now, when people in Britain are diagnosed by doctors as having malaria, they are people who have recently been travelling overseas to places where mosquitoes still carry the disease.

In days gone by, malaria, a disease in which the patient suffers from high fever and sweats a great deal, was common in Europe. It used to be known as 'ague'. The earliest records of the disease date back to the fifth century

A malaria-carrying mosquito

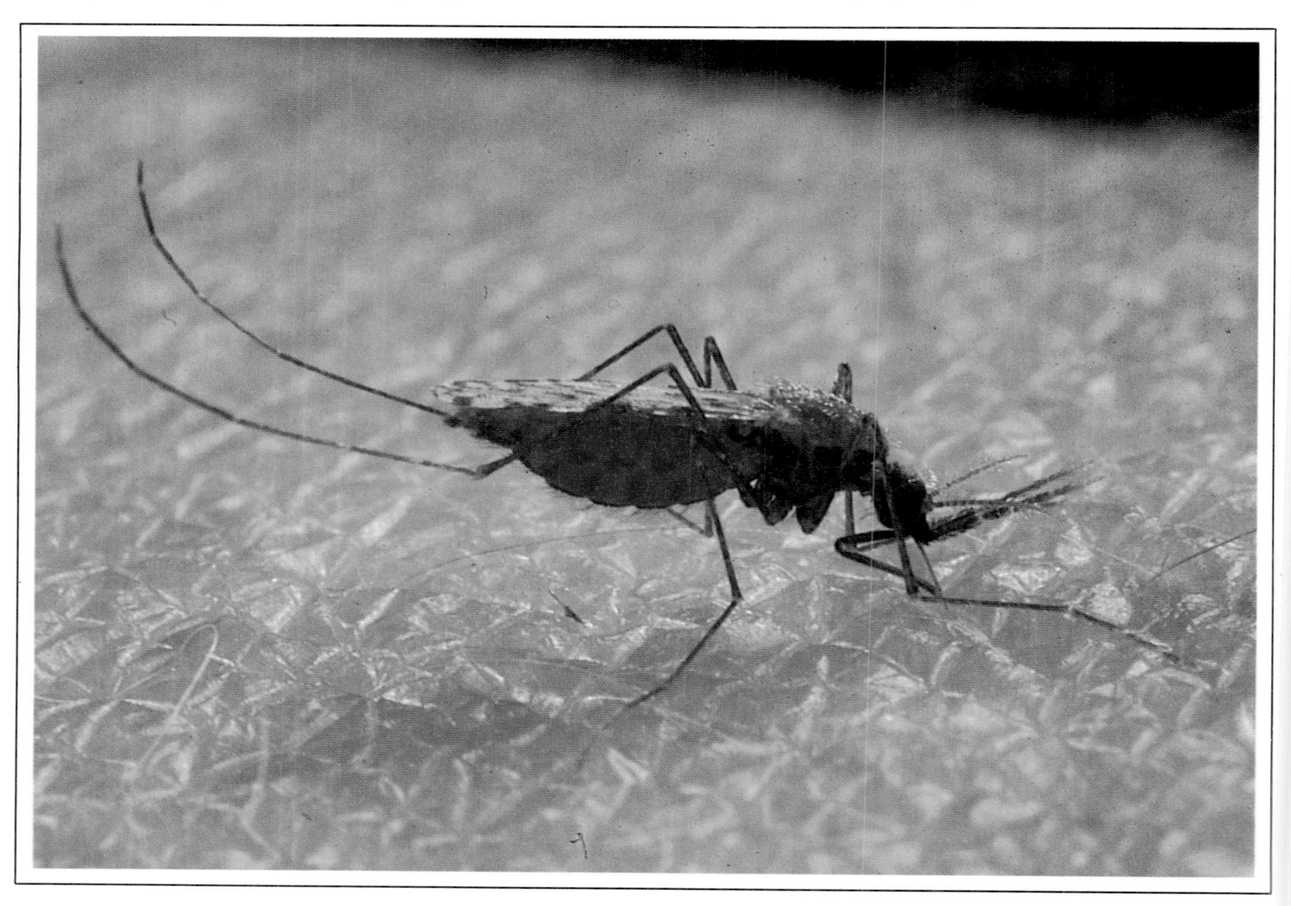

BC, when the Greek physician Hippocrates wrote about various kinds of fever. Some historians believe that widespread epidemics of malaria helped to cause the fall of the Roman Empire! The word 'malaria' comes from the Italian for 'bad air' and it was long ago thought to be caused by just that. It isn't, though the damp air of marshes and other bodies of water provides mosquitoes with the water they need in order to breed. Both the malaria parasite and the mosquito need man to be able to survive and prosper.

Mosquito eggs are deposited in water. After 2–3 days the larvae hatch out, and they spend the next few weeks near the surface of the water, breathing air through a sort of snorkel tube (like that used by deep-sea divers) at both ends of their bodies and eating tiny living creatures in the water. So that it can grow, the larva sheds its outer casing 4 times, and after that it hardens into a pupa. After 3–4 days the pupa hatches into an adult mosquito. To begin with the mosquito drifts around using the pupa case as a raft while it waits for its wings to dry. When it has dried out properly, it is able to fly. Once in the air, male and female mosquitoes mate, and then, while the males go off to feed on plant-juices, the females set out in search of human blood! The female mosquito has piercing and cutting mouth-parts and injects saliva as she feeds on her victim. If the victim is suffering from malaria, the malaria parasite is present in the blood and enters the stomach of the mosquito as

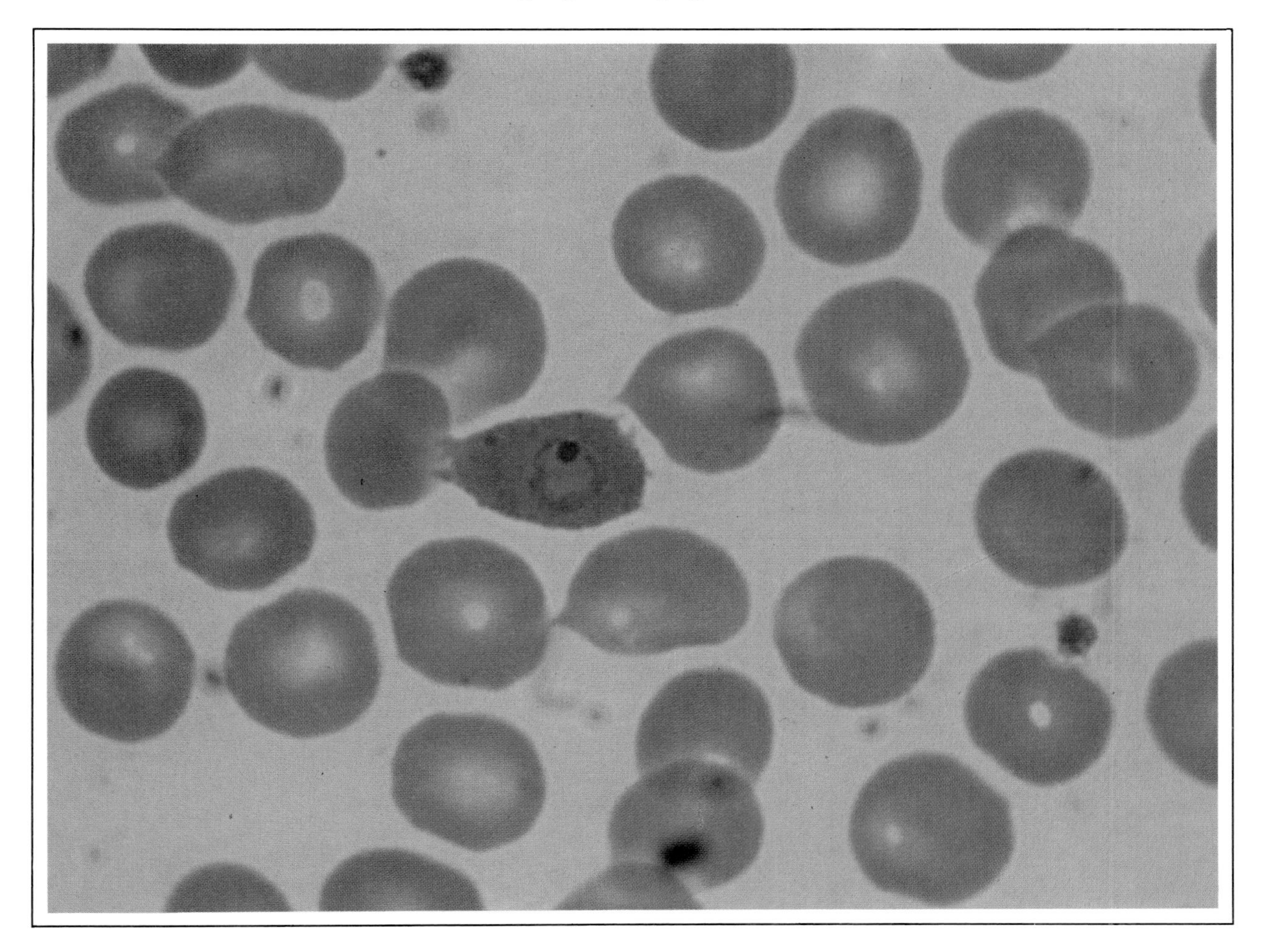

Malaria parasites in human blood

The life-cycle of a mosquito

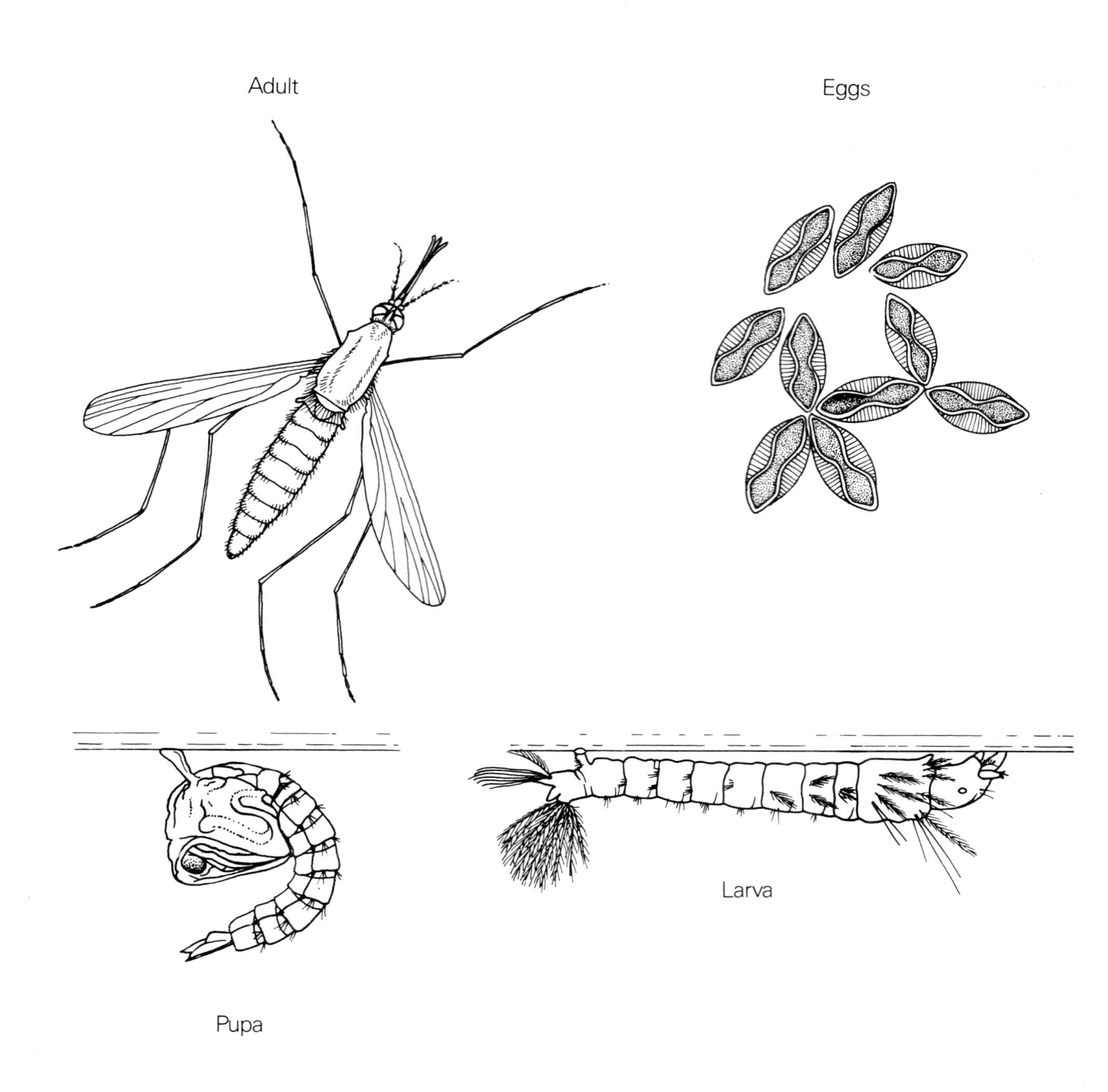

she feeds. Once it is there, the tiny protozoan undergoes changes and multiplies over a period of 1–3 weeks. The malaria parasites then move to the saliva glands of the mosquito. When the female mosquito takes her next meal, the parasites are injected into the victim with her saliva. They travel through the blood to the liver, where they multiply again and then invade the red blood-cells, where they multiply yet again. The multiplying of the parasite breaks open and destroys the red cell. It is the damage done to the liver and the